Paul Mueller
arch.

DESCRIPTIVE GEOMETRY
FOR
ARCHITECTS AND BUILDERS

BY

LESLIE A. LEE, L.I.O.B., M.R.San.I., A.B.I.C.C.
City and Guilds Hons.—Silver Medallist (Carpentry and Joinery)

SENIOR LECTURER OF BUILDING COURSE,
THE POLYTECHNIC SCHOOL OF ARCHITECTURE, SURVEYING AND BUILDING, LONDON

AND

R. FRASER REEKIE, F.R.I.B.A., Dip. Arch., Architect
R.I.B.A. Bossom Gold and Silver Medallist
R.I.B.A. Grissell Gold Medallist (Advanced Construction)

FORMERLY INSTRUCTOR IN DRAUGHTSMANSHIP, LECTURER IN DESIGN AND CONSTRUCTION,
THE POLYTECHNIC SCHOOL OF ARCHITECTURE, SURVEYING AND BUILDING, LONDON

LONDON
EDWARD ARNOLD (PUBLISHERS) LTD

REPRINTED BY LITHOGRAPHY IN GREAT BRITAIN BY JARROLD AND SONS LTD.,
NORWICH

PREFACE

In the preparation of this book full consideration has been given to the needs of those preparing for or engaged in the building industry, and the aim has been to provide a sound knowledge of the principles of geometry and geometrical drawing, and their various practical applications.

The illustrations and diagrams, which include many examples of present-day building practice, are simple and clear, and the text has been kept as brief as possible consistent with adequate descriptions and explanations; the author's experiences having shown that understanding of the problems is thereby made easier.

Every endeavour has been made to cover fully the work on which are based the examination questions of the City and Guilds, London (Trades), the Union of Lancashire and Cheshire Institutes, and the Union of Educational Institutes, which bodies have kindly given permission for the reproduction of examination questions at the end of the book.

We also wish to acknowledge with thanks the use of the illustrations of the surveying instruments and theodolite, provided by Messrs. Cooke, Troughton and Simms, Ltd., London.

Leslie A. Lee
R. Fraser Reekie

CONTENTS

PLATES

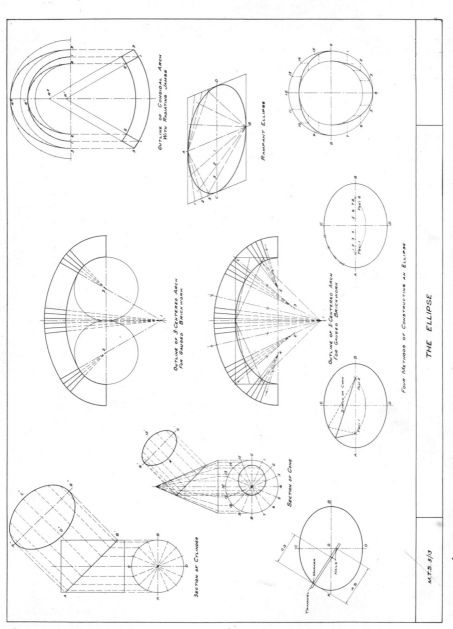

OUTLINE OF CONOIDAL ARCH WITH RADIATING JAMBS

RAMPANT ELLIPSE

OUTLINE OF 3 CENTERED ARCH FOR GAUGED BRICKWORK

OUTLINE OF 5 CENTERED ARCH FOR GAUGED BRICKWORK

FOUR METHODS OF CONSTRUCTING AN ELLIPSE

THE ELLIPSE

SECTION OF CYLINDER

SECTION OF CONE

M.T.S. 5/13

STUDENT'S DRAWING ILLUSTRATING WELL-ARRANGED AND WELL DRAWN EXERCISES DEALING WITH THE ELLIPSE. THE ORIGINAL DRAWING IS IMPERIAL SIZE

INTRODUCTION

THE word "Geometry" comes from two Greek words: "GE"—the earth, and "METRIA"—measuring, and the term shows the original use of the science for purposes of land surveying, for which it is still the fundamental basis. But it also forms the foundation of any education in building design and construction. The architect needs to know and comprehend shapes, enclosed spaces and solids, and their representation by means of drawings, particularly new planning forms and elements resulting from modern scientific structural methods and principles of design. The builder and craftsman need geometry for the setting out of works and details, and for an infinite number of practical applications to construction.

Measuring

A surface or a solid object is measured by finding how many times it contains a suitable unit: for example, a short distance or small area would be measured in feet, inches and parts of an inch, whilst a long distance in miles, furlongs, yards, etc.

The common units of English linear measurement are:

12 inches	= 1 foot	(7·92 inches—1 link)
3 feet	= 1 yard	
5½ yards	= 1 pole	(25 links)
4 poles	= 1 chain	
40 poles	= 1 furlong	
10 chains	= 1 furlong	
8 furlongs	= 1 mile	(1760 yards)

In some countries the "metric" system of linear measurement is used:

10 millimetres	= 1 centimetre
10 centimetres	= 1 metre (39·3708 inches)
10 metres	= 1 decimetre
10 decimetres	= 1 hectometre
10 hectometres	= 1 kilometre

The common units of English square (area) measurement are:

144 square inches	= 1 square foot
9 square feet	= 1 square yard
30¼ square yards	= 1 square rod, pole or perch
40 square rods	= 1 rood
4 roods	= 1 acre
640 acres	= 1 square mile

Measuring Equipment

For measuring distances, areas, and objects, the following may be used:

(a) *Rules* of various kinds, e.g. divided into inches and parts of an inch, or divided into feet and inches (including 2 ft., 3 ft., and 5 ft. folding rules).

(b) *Tapes*, measuring feet and inches.

(c) *"Chain"* (66 feet) and arrows—chiefly used for land measurement. 100 "links" to a chain, 66 feet, is a unit common to both linear and square measure. An "Engineer's Chain," 50 ft. or 100 ft., is also used for land measure.

(d) *Line* or *Cord*.

(e) *Callipers*, for circular objects.

Drawing Equipment

The drawings prepared by architects, surveyors and builders have, in the main, a geometrical basis and need to be drawn with care and accuracy, using drawing-board, tee-square, set-squares, and instruments. The illustration (Plate I) shows the equipment ready for use.

Drawing-board. Should be of good quality with perfectly true edges. Imperial size is the most useful for work described in this book.

Tee-square. Preferably of mahogany with ebony or celluloid ruling edge, which should be bevelled. Size to fit board, i.e. imperial.

Set-squares. Either two plain celluloid ones of 45 degrees and 60 degrees respectively, or an adjustable set-square which can be set to any angle. Set-squares should have sides of not less than 6″, and should be square-edged, not bevelled.

Protractor. Not essential, but sometimes useful for measuring angles if an adjustable set-square is not available.

Drawing Instruments. These are probably the most costly items of equipment, as good instruments are essential for satisfactory work. They can be bought in sets or purchased separately. The latter is generally the better method and less expensive. Required are: dividers—4″ or more long; compasses, with interchangeable pencil, pen and divider points; spring-bow dividers; spring-bow pen and pencil compasses; and ruling pen for ink lines.

Scale. 12″ or 6″ long, made of boxwood or ivory and divided into units and twelfths of $\frac{1}{8}″$, $\frac{1}{4}″$, $\frac{3}{8}″$, $\frac{1}{2}″$, $\frac{3}{4}″$, 1″, $1\frac{1}{2}″$ and 3″.

Pencils. Best quality only should be used. If properly sharpened and handled, grades *HB* and *H* will meet all normal purposes Points should be about $\frac{3}{4}″$ long, of which $\frac{1}{4}″$ should

PLATE I

DRAWING EQUIPMENT: DRAWING BOARD, TEE-SQUARE, SET-SQUARES, SCALE AND VARIOUS INSTRUMENTS ARE SHOWN IN THE ILLUSTRATION OF A DRAUGHTSMAN AT WORK

be exposed lead sharpened to a round point. A penknife is best for sharpening. The point will last longer if the pencil is revolved slowly in ruling lines.

Erasers. Soft rubbers should be used in correcting pencil errors; special hard rubbers for ink lines.

Drawing Papers. There are many kinds and qualities of drawing papers. Good quality cartridge paper is satisfactory for the work described in this book and for most uncoloured pencil and ink drawings.

Procedure

In commencing a drawing the first operation is to pin down carefully and squarely the paper to the board, using small flat-headed drawing pins. Lines should then be drawn around the sheet about $\frac{3}{4}''$ in from the edges to form a border, and also for use as check lines if the paper is removed from the board before completion and re-set.

Careful consideration should be given to the scale to be used and to the arrangement of the drawing—perhaps necessitating a trial setting out on tracing paper.

The systematic laying out of the various parts of a drawing, namely: plans, elevations, sections, etc., will be dealt with in the chapter on Orthographic Projection.

Note: It is necessary in dealing with geometrical diagrams to use figures and letters to indicate the located points of the drawings. To avoid confusion, the letter "I" is omitted from the examples that follow.

CHAPTER I
SCALES

Division of Lines; Construction and Use of Scales, Linear,
Diagonal, Vernier; Scale of Chords and Measurement of
Angles

In practical Geometry and in drawing plans, elevations and
sections of objects and buildings it is necessary to use scales.
Scales are constructed by dividing straight lines into appropriate
units of length proportionate to actual units of measurement.

Definition of Lines

A line is considered to have length but no breadth; therefore,
a drawn line which must have breadth is mathematically incorrect,
but the middle of such a line is taken as the real line. A straight
line is the shortest distance ruled between two points.

Division of Lines

Fig. 1 shows how any line AB can be divided into a number
of equal parts. The method is to draw a line at an acute angle
from A, and along this to plot equal units of any convenient
dimension—8 are shown in the example—by the use of dividers
or scale. From the end of the last of these units, marked C, a line
is drawn to B, and parallel to it other lines are drawn from the
intermediate points dividing AB into 8 equal parts.

Fig. 2 shows how a length of board of any width can be divided
into a number of equal units by placing a rule diagonally across
it so that convenient equal divisions can be marked off.

Fig. 3 shows how any straight line can be bisected (divided
into two equal parts). Using compasses and taking A and B, the
ends of the line, as centres, and with any radius greater than half
AB, two arcs are drawn to intersect on either side of the line.
A straight line joining these intersections bisects AB.

Construction of Scales

Fig. 4 shows examples of common scales in which inches or
parts of an inch represent larger units of measurement:

4

DIVISION OF LINES

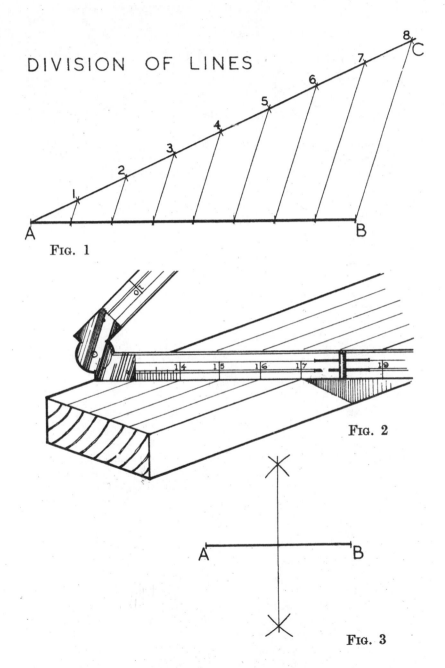

FIG. 1

FIG. 2

FIG. 3

$\frac{1}{8}''$ equals 1' 0" (8 ft. to 1 in.) $\frac{1}{96}$ representative fraction
$\frac{1}{2}''$ equals 1' 0" (2 ft. to 1 in.) $\frac{1}{24}$,,   ,,
1"   equals 1' 0" (1 ft. to 1 in.) $\frac{1}{12}$,,   ,,
$1\frac{1}{2}''$ equals 1' 0" $\frac{1}{8}$,,   ,,
3"   equals 1' 0" $\frac{1}{4}$,,   ,,
1"   equals 1 mile
1"   equals 10 paces

In the construction of these scales it may be found simplest to rule straight lines and mark off the required units from a rule or draughtsman's scale. As shown, the first unit of each scale is subdivided into a number of fractions; for example, in the scale of $1\frac{1}{2}''$ equals 1' 0", the first unit is divided into twelfths—each actually $\frac{1}{8}''$—representing inches.

(Note: A definite reading has been indicated on each scale.)

The following are the usual scales for architects', builders' and surveyors' drawings:

For lay-outs, site plans, 41·6 ft. to 1 in. ($\frac{1}{500}$ natural scale).
For plans, elevations and sections of large buildings, 8 ft. to 1 in.
For   ,,   ,,   ,,   small   ,,   4 ft. to 1 in.
For details, particularly working drawings   2 ft. to 1 in.
For isolated details   1 ft. to 1 in.
For workshop drawings, Full Size Details (F.S.D.) are required.
As used on Ordnance Maps
  General Map of the
    United Kingdom,   1 in. to 1 mile ($\frac{1}{63360}$ natural scale)
    County Maps,   6 ins. to 1 mile ($\frac{1}{10560}$,,   ,,   )
    Cadastral or Parish Maps,   25·344 ins. to 1 mile ($\frac{1}{2500}$,,   ,,   )
                            60 ins. to 1 mile ($\frac{1}{1056}$,,   ,,   )
                         120 ins. to 1 mile ($\frac{1}{528}$,,   ,,   )
                 126·720 ins. to 1 mile ($\frac{1}{500}$,,   ,,   )

Diagonal Scales

These scales are particularly useful where small subdivisions are necessary. The surveyor, for instance, finds a diagonal scale of value in setting out a field survey in chains and links at, say, the scale $1\frac{1}{2}''$ equals 1 chain—see Fig. 7.

Fig. 5 shows a diagonal scale representing hundredths of an inch. The method of constructing such a scale is to mark off on a straight line a number of one-inch units according to the length of scale required. The first unit AB is then subdivided into ten equal parts, i.e. each part represents ten-hundredths of an inch. The width of the scale marked AD, which may be any convenient dimension, is also divided into ten equal parts. A diagonal line is drawn from the point marked 90 to D, and parallel diagonal lines from points 80, 70, 60 and so on. Readings can be taken to a hundredth part of an inch along the horizontal lines as illustrated by the example given of a precise dimension.

12" 0 1' 2'   10'   20'

1/8 INCH = 1 FOOT

12" 6" 0   1'   2'   3'   4'   5'   6'

3'-6"

1/2 INCH = 1 FOOT

12" 9" 6" 3" 0   1'   2'

1'-9"

1 INCH = 1 FOOT

12" 9" 6" 3" 0   1'

1'-9"

1 1/2 INCHES = 1 FOOT

12"   9"   6"   3"   0

10"

3 INCHES = 1 FOOT

8 FURLONGS   0   1   2 MILES

2 MILES 4 FURLONGS

1 INCH = 1 MILE

10 PACES 5   0   10   20

16 PACES

1 INCH = 10 PACES

SCALES   FIG. 4

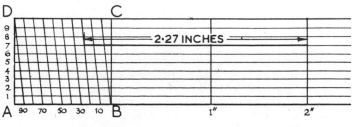

2·27 INCHES

DIAGONAL SCALE   FIG. 5

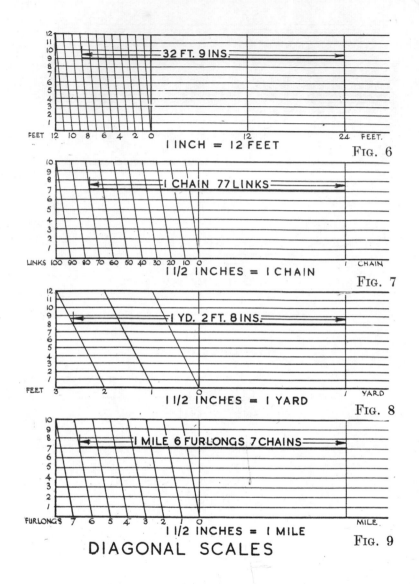

FIG. 6

1 INCH = 12 FEET

FIG. 7

1 1/2 INCHES = 1 CHAIN

FIG. 8

1 1/2 INCHES = 1 YARD

FIG. 9

1 1/2 INCHES = 1 MILE

DIAGONAL SCALES

Figs. 6 to 9 show the following diagonal scales:

1″ equals 12′ 0″, to be read in feet and inches
1½″ equals 1 chain, to be read in chains and links
1½″ equals 1 yard, to be read in yards, feet and inches
1½″ equals 1 mile, to be read in miles, furlongs and chains

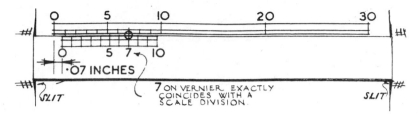

FIG. 10

The Vernier Scale

By means of this type of scale small fractions of a unit can be read. It is adapted for various purposes. For example, the theodolite, a surveying instrument used for measuring angles, has commonly a dial marked with units of degrees and minutes, and a vernier attachment divided into units of 20 seconds, making it possible to measure angles in degrees, minutes and 20 seconds. An illustration of the theodolite is shown in Fig. 25. With certain types of theodolites it is possible to obtain readings to the fraction of 10 seconds. Weight-testing machines similarly have vernier scales usually to read tons, hundredweights and pounds.

Fig. 10 illustrates the working of the vernier scale. The main scale is a simply constructed scale divided into inches and tenths of an inch. The vernier is set out accurately on a separate part and made 9/10″ long, and is divided into 10 equal parts. It is made to slide under the main scale by being inserted in the slits indicated. If 0 on the vernier is under 0 on the main scale, then 10 on the vernier will coincide with 9 on the main scale. If the vernier is moved along until, say, the seventh unit coincides exactly with some division on the main scale, the reading (the distance from the end of the vernier to the previous subdivision on the main scale) will be 7/10 of 1/10,. i.e. 7/100″ or ·07 inches. The reading is always found by noting which division on the vernier exactly coincides with a division on the main scale.

A useful exercise is the construction of a vernier scale to read degrees and minutes, as used on the theodolite. Firstly, a suitable radius is determined and the arc of a circle described. On it are marked, using a protractor for quickness, units of degrees, which are subdivided into 3 equal units of 20 minutes. The vernier is made with its length 20 minutes less than 20 degree units. It is divided into 20 equal units. which are again each subdivided into 3 equal units. Fig. 11 shows such a scale with the vernier placed to read 20 minutes. Fig. 12 shows the vernier to read 4 degrees

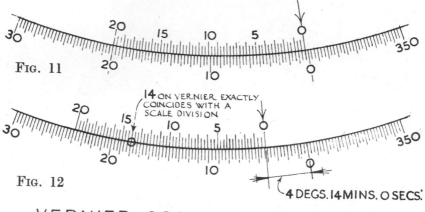

Fig. 11

Fig. 12

14 ON VERNIER EXACTLY
COINCIDES WITH A
SCALE DIVISION

4 DEGS. 14 MINS. O SECS.

VERNIER SCALES

14 minutes 0 seconds (the reading can be seen to lie between 4 degrees and 4 degrees 20 minutes; division 14 on the vernier exactly coincides with a division on the main scale).

Scale of Chords

This scale can be used for setting out any required angle or for measuring the number of degrees of any angle.

Fig. 13 shows a scale of chords. The scale is constructed by drawing the quadrant of a circle (quarter circle) with any convenient radius, hence AB equals AC. The arc CB is divided into 9 equal units by using a protractor, or first into 3 equal units using 60°–30° set-square and then into smaller units by trial and error, using dividers. Each unit represents 10 degrees; further subdivision into single degrees can be made by bisection or by using dividers. Using compasses, with B as centre, arcs of circles are drawn from the divisions to the line AB, and thence vertically to the scale.

To illustrate the use of the scale, if two lines AB, AC are set out to form any acute angle, as shown in Fig. 14, and by means of compasses or dividers the length of the scale 0 degrees to 60 degrees is marked along them from A, then the distance from B to C measured and read on the scale gives the angle formed by the lines.

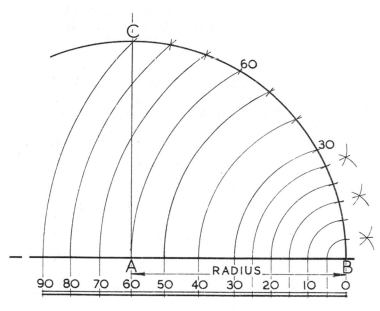

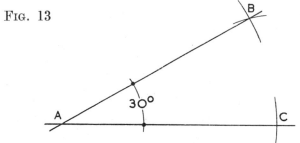

FIG. 13

FIG. 14

SCALE OF CHORDS

CHAPTER II

TRIANGLES AND ANGLES

CONSTRUCTION OF TRIANGLES; PLANE TABLE; BOX SEXTANT;
TRAVERSE SURVEYS; USE OF THEODOLITE; LEVELLING

A TRIANGLE is a plane figure having 3 sides, and therefore three
angles. The various types of triangles are shown in Fig. 15:
(A) right-angled, (B) equilateral, (C) isosceles, (D) acute and obtuse
scalene.

The sum of the angles of any triangle equals 180 degrees. A
right-angle triangle has two sides at right-angles to each other;
the two remaining angles together equal 90 degrees. The equilateral triangle having three equal sides has three angles of 60
degrees. The isosceles triangle has two equal angles and two sides
of the same dimension. Scalene triangles have three unequal sides
and three unequal angles.

Construction of Equilateral Triangle

Draw the base line, EF, as in Fig. 15; with compasses of radius
EF and centre E describe an arc, and with the same radius and
centre F describe another arc cutting the first at G. By joining
E and F to G the triangle is completed.

Construction of a Triangle with sides of given length

The required triangle ABC has sides of, say, AB equal to $3\frac{1}{2}''$,
AC equal to $2\frac{1}{2}''$, BC equal to $3''$. Draw base line AB; with compasses of radius $2\frac{1}{2}''$ and with centre A describe an arc; adjust
compasses to radius of $3''$ and with centre B describe another arc
cutting the first at C; join AB and BC to complete triangle.
In the case of an isosceles triangle sides AC and BC would
be equal.

The use of triangles in practical Geometry will be dealt with
in later chapters. The following refer to the use of triangles in
Surveying.

The Plane Table

This is a simple instrument for making approximate surveys,
and is used in connection with military sketches. It consists of
a small drawing-board fixed to a tripod so that a sighting rule or
"alidade" can be levelled and plumbed in any position. A sheet

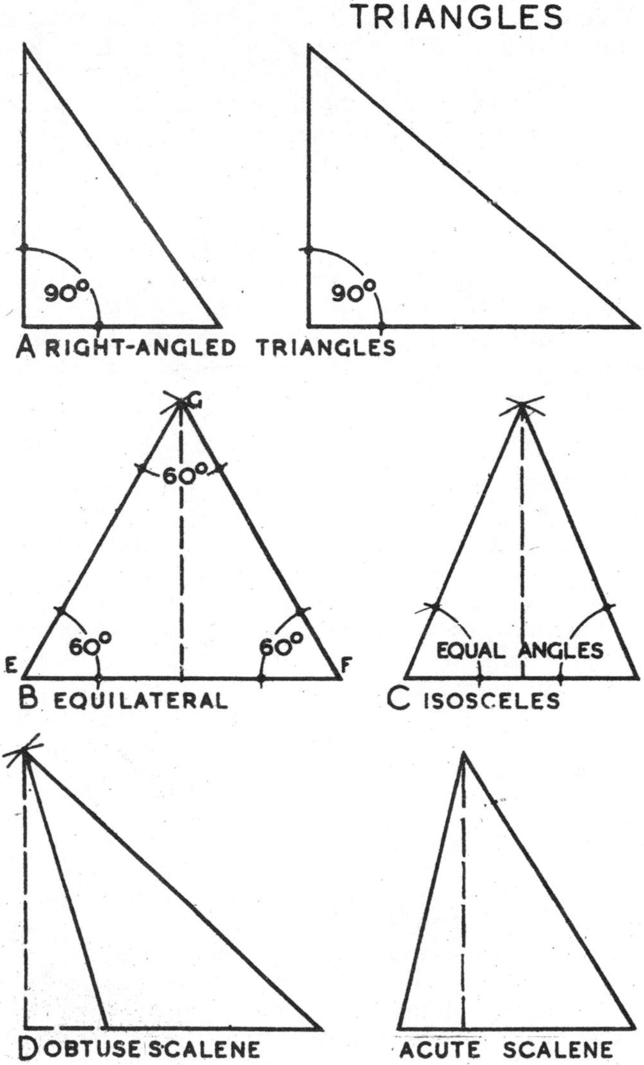

TRIANGLES

A RIGHT-ANGLED TRIANGLES

B EQUILATERAL

C ISOSCELES

EQUAL ANGLES

D OBTUSE SCALENE

ACUTE SCALENE

Fig. 15

of drawing paper is pinned to the board and by means of the "alidade," the direction of any object can be marked on the paper. Fig. 16 shows a sketch of the plane table with ranging poles staked into the ground at various points, $C\ D\ E\ F$, known as "stations." The tripod is plumb over a wood peg, A, temporarily replacing a ranging pole. Sight lines are taken to the stations $C\ D\ E\ F$ and B and ruled on the paper, Fig. 17. The distance AB, the base line, is measured and drawn to a suitable scale, say 88' 0" to 1", on the paper in the correct positions. The plane table, etc., is then moved and placed plumb over station point B. The sight lines are taken as before and the directions drawn on the paper. The result is the formation of a series of triangles on the paper, all with the common base, AB, and with apices giving to scale the positions of $C\ D\ E\ F$, the distances of which can be measured. The acreage of the land surveyed can also be found by simple calculation.

The Box Sextant

Another method of surveying land is that in which the box sextant is used. A full description is not possible here, but it is about 3" in diameter, sometimes with a telescope attached. It is fitted with a scale and vernier curved to a flat arc, radius 2", of about 150 degrees; the scale commences at 5 degrees below zero and is divided into degrees and half degrees. The vernier is the length of 29 of these degrees and is divided into 30 equal parts, thus enabling angles to be read in degrees and minutes—the reading being made with the help of a magnifying glass. With some models it is only possible to read angles up to 90 degrees, and consequently intermediate settings are necessary if greater angles are required.

Traverse Survey using the Box Sextant

The use of the box sextant is illustrated in Fig. 18. A stream forms the boundary of a field and it is required to plot its winding course. A number of ranging poles are placed at convenient positions as near as is practicable to the edge of the stream with the object of making a series of triangles which will tie each other forming a traverse survey. Commencing at station point A and proceeding in the direction indicated by the arrows the box sextant is held close to the ranging poles and the readings of the angles indicated are made and booked, afterwards being drawn on paper. The box sextant is not accurate for trigonometrical surveys, but it is a useful check on chain surveys. The theodolite is the most accurate instrument.

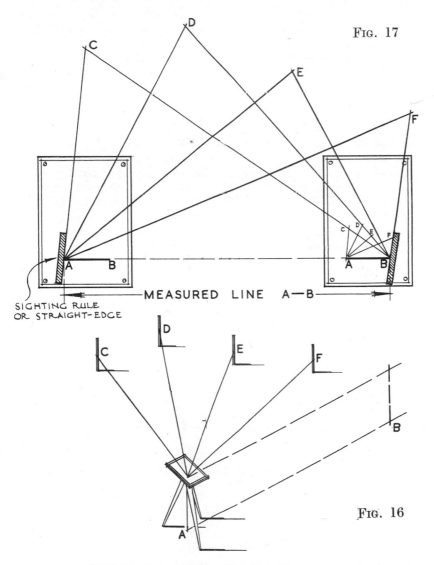

Fig. 17

MEASURED LINE A—B

SIGHTING RULE
OR STRAIGHT-EDGE

Fig. 16

THE PLANE TABLE

Traverse Survey using Chain

Fig. 19 shows the method of making a simple traverse survey using the "Gunter's" Chain (100 links) or an "Engineers" Chain (in feet). Ranging poles are placed as before. Commencing at station A, running dimensions are taken in the direction indicated by the arrows and booked in the appropriate column of a field book. Offset measurements are also taken at frequent intervals at right-angles to the chain and from it to the edge of the stream. These measurements are likewise recorded in the field book. Fig. 20 shows part of such recordings as set out in the field book.

Setting out a Right-angle using a Chain or Tape

Fig. 21 shows the method as it might be used for setting out the centre lines of foundation trenches for a rectangular building. A wooden peg is driven into the ground at A, the point of inter-section of the centre lines of two trenches. A distance of, say, 3' 0" is measured in the known direction of one trench, and another peg is driven into the ground at B. A tape is then passed round the pegs, and pulled tight in such a way that a triangle is

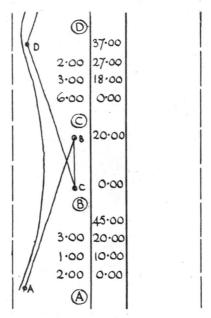

FIELD BOOK

Fig. 20

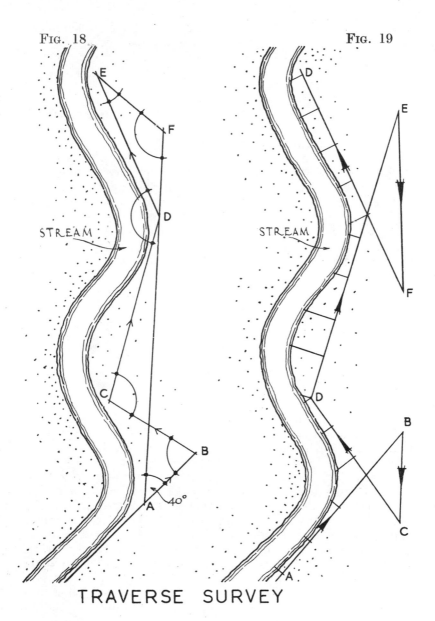

FIG. 18   FIG. 19

STREAM

STREAM

40°

TRAVERSE SURVEY

formed with sides 3' 0", 4' 0" and 5' 0" long, thus giving point C, and angle B A C equal to 90 degrees.

The basis of this method, in which any suitable measurements can be taken, is the well-known "Theorem of Pythagorus," i.e. that, in a right-angled triangle, the square on the hypotenuse equals the sum of the squares on the other two sides (see Fig. 22).

The Clinometer

Instruments for measuring slopes are known as clinometers. The best known is the theodolite, which is also used for measuring flat angles as previously mentioned.

To Find Heights using a Theodolite

In Fig. 23 the height of a tall building, chimney-stack, cliff, etc., marked A B, is to be found. The theodolite is set up on the ground some measured distance away, and the instrument is made level, with the centre of the telescope horizontal to the scale, i.e. at zero. The telescope is then carefully raised until it is sighted on point B; the *angle of elevation* can then be read on the scale, and by a scale drawing or by trigonometrical calculation the height required can be found. It is necessary, of course, to include for the height of the instrument from the ground.

The same principle is illustrated in Fig. 24, in which the *angle of depression* is found as a basis for the calculations.

Fig. 25 shows the general appearance of the theodolite.

Levelling

Levelling may be defined as the determining of the rise and fall of any land, etc., from a known datum, which may be an official bench mark as found on ordnance maps.

Fig. 26 illustrates the general method of working. It is required to find the fall of land from a given datum. A builder's or dumpy level is set up in a position so that a reading can be taken to a level staff placed on the datum—(a level staff is in three telescopic units extending to 14' 0", and is read in feet, tenths of feet and hundredths of feet). This reading is known as a *back-sight*. Leaving the instrument in the same position, the staff is moved onwards to measure points known as *intermediate sights*, and readings are taken until the farthest measure point to which a reading can be obtained is reached. This last is known as the *fore-sight*. The staff is now held firm and steady while the instrument is moved to a point farther on from which a reading back to the staff can be obtained. The previous procedure is repeated, and so on until the last reading, in this case Peg. No. 7, a fore-sight, is made. (Flying levels can finally be taken in unmeasured distances from Peg. No. 7 to the datum for a check.)

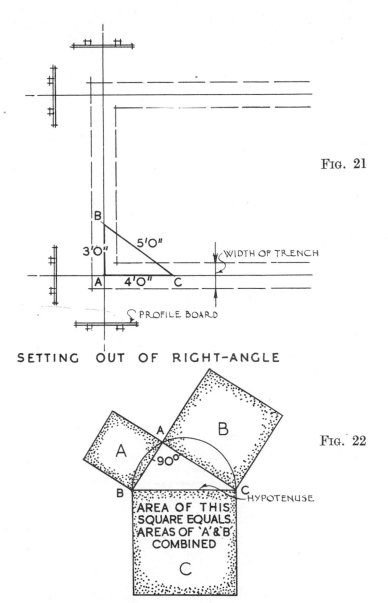

FIG. 21

WIDTH OF TRENCH

B

3'0" 5'0"

A 4'0" C

PROFILE BOARD

SETTING OUT OF RIGHT-ANGLE

A

B

90°

B C HYPOTENUSE

AREA OF THIS
SQUARE EQUALS
AREAS OF 'A'&'B'
COMBINED

C

FIG. 22

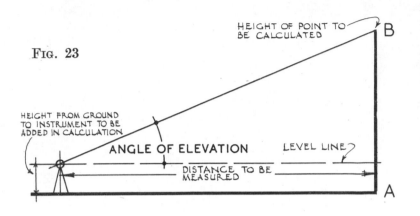

Fig. 23

HEIGHT OF POINT TO BE CALCULATED

B

HEIGHT FROM GROUND TO INSTRUMENT TO BE ADDED IN CALCULATION

ANGLE OF ELEVATION

LEVEL LINE

DISTANCE TO BE MEASURED

A

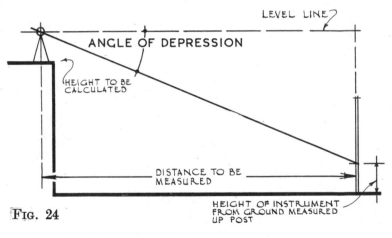

LEVEL LINE

ANGLE OF DEPRESSION

HEIGHT TO BE CALCULATED

DISTANCE TO BE MEASURED

HEIGHT OF INSTRUMENT FROM GROUND MEASURED UP POST

Fig. 24

MEASUREMENT OF HEIGHTS

PLATE II

FIG. 25. A THEODOLITE

PLATE III

FIG. 29. A LEVEL

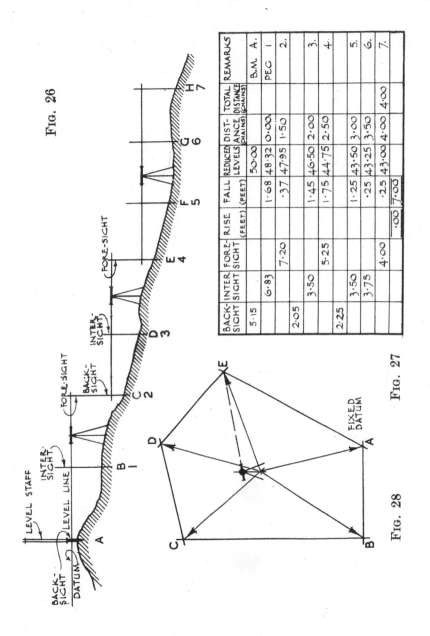

FIG. 26

FIG. 27

BACK-SIGHT	INTER-SIGHT	FORE-SIGHT	RISE (FEET)	FALL (FEET)	REDUCED LEVELS	DIST-ANCE (CHAINS)	TOTAL DISTANCE (CHAINS)	REMARKS
5·15					50·00			B.M. A.
	6·83			1·68	48·32	0·00	0·00	PEG 1.
		7·20		·37	47·95	1·50	1·50	2.
2·05	3·50			1·45	46·50	2·00	2·00	3.
		5·25		1·75	44·75	2·50	2·50	4.
2·25	3·50			1·25	43·50	3·00	3·00	5.
	3·75			·25	43·25	3·50	3·50	6.
		4·00		·25	43·00	4·00	4·00	7.
			·00	7·00				

FIG. 28

Fig. 27 shows the level book for such a line. The difference between the totals in the rise and fall columns should be the same as the difference between the first and last readings in the red iced levels column.

Spot Levels

Fig. 28 shows how it is possible to take a series of readings to complete a level line on points on the boundary of a piece of land without moving the level. This is known as taking spot land readings. Assuming a start is made at a known back-sight or bench mark, A, then the last reading will be taken as a fore-sight to the same point.

Fig. 29, facing page 21, shows the general appearance of a modern level.

CHAPTER III

PLANE FIGURES

QUADRILATERALS—SQUARE, RECTANGLES, PARALLELOGRAMS, ETC.
POLYGONS. USE IN CONNECTION WITH SURVEYING INSTRUMENTS.

Quadrilaterals

A quadrilateral is a plane figure having four straight sides, but when such a figure has two sides which are equal and parallel it is better known as a *parallelogram*. In any parallelogram: (1) the opposite sides are equal, (2) the opposite angles are equal, (3) any two adjacent angles equal 180 degrees, and all four angles make 360 degrees, (4) either diagonal divides the figure into similar triangles, (5) the diagonals bisect each other. The four parallelograms shown in Fig. 30 are:

(a) The *square*, which has four equal sides and its angles are right-angles.

(b) The *rectangle* (oblong), which has equal opposite sides and its angles are right-angles.

(c) The *rhombus*, which has four equal sides, but its angles are not right-angles.

(d) The *rhomboid*, which has equal opposite sides, but its angles are not right-angles.

These parallelograms can be set out in various ways. The easiest method of constructing a square is by the use of tee-square and 45 degree set-square. In Fig. 30 (A), if *A B* is the base of the required square, perpendicular lines are erected at *A* and *B*, and a line is drawn at 45 degrees from *B* to cut the perpendicular from *A* in *C*; a line is drawn parallel to *A B* from *C* cutting the perpendicular from *B* in *D*, thus completing the square, *A B C D*. Fig. 30 (A₁) shows an alternative method. The base line *A B* is drawn; perpendicular lines are erected at *A* and *B* by the use of compasses, as shown, and the distance *A B* marked on them giving points *C* and *D*, by joining which the square is completed.

The rectangle can be similarly constructed. A variation, Fig. 30 (B), is to draw the base line *A B*; then, with radius equal to the perpendicular height and centres at *A* and *B* two arcs are described; perpendiculars are erected from *A* and *B* to cut these arcs in *C* and *D*, the joining of which completes the figure.

Fig. 30 (C) shows the construction of the rhombus. The base line *A B* is drawn; with centre *A* and radius *A B* an arc is described and a line is drawn from *A* to cut the arc in *C* to form the required angle CAB; from C and B, with radius AB, arcs are described intersecting at D. By joining C and B to D the figure is completed.

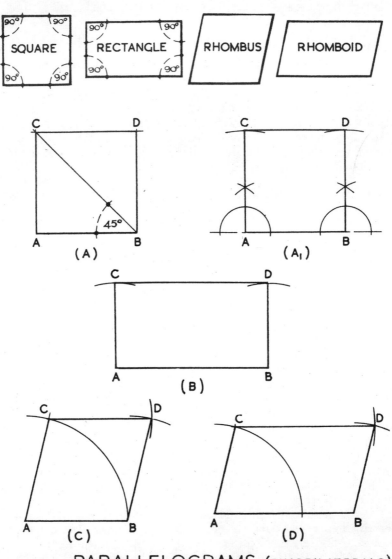

PARALLELOGRAMS (QUADRILATERALS)

FIG. 30

Fig. 30 (D) shows the construction of the rhomboid in a similar manner to the foregoing, allowance being made for the difference in length of adjacent sides.

Two other quadrilaterals, shown in Fig. 31, are:

(a) The *trapezoid*, which has only two sides parallel.
(b) The *trapezium*, which has no parallel sides.

The construction of these figures as indicated follows the methods employed for the previous figures.

Use of Quadrilaterals in Surveying

Fig. 32 shows a field having a boundary with four sides. To survey this field ranging poles are staked at the corners *A, B, C, D,* The straight distances, indicated by the arrows, are measured using the chain, and diagonal ties or checks are also measured. Offsets are taken to the boundary in the manner explained in Chapter II.

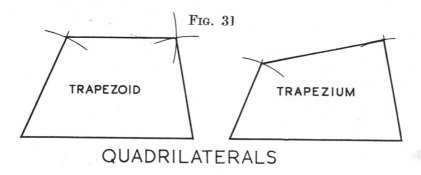

FIG. 31

TRAPEZOID

TRAPEZIUM

QUADRILATERALS

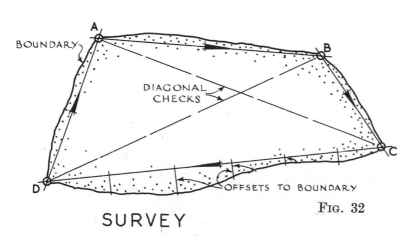

BOUNDARY

DIAGONAL CHECKS

OFFSETS TO BOUNDARY

FIG. 32

SURVEY

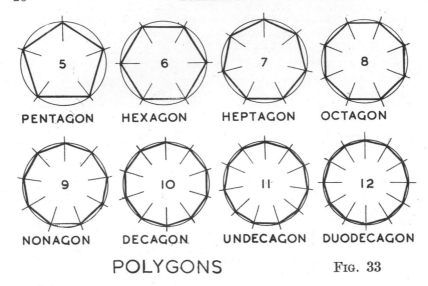

POLYGONS

FIG. 33

Polygons

The figures known as polygons have five or more sides, and can be characterised as regular polygons and irregular polygons. The former have sides of equal dimension and equal interior angles; the latter have unequal sides and angles.

Polygons are named according to the number of sides and angles. Shown in Fig. 33 are:

> The *pentagon*, which has five sides.
> The *hexagon*, which has six sides.
> The *heptagon*, which has seven sides.
> The *octagon*, which has eight sides.
> The *nonagon*, which has nine sides.
> The *decagon*, which has ten sides.
> The *undecagon*, which has eleven sides.
> The *duodecagon*, which has twelve sides.

The hexagon, octagon and duodecagon are most commonly used in building forms.

It is useful to remember that the sum of the interior angles of any polygon is equal to twice as many right-angles as the polygon has sides, minus the four right-angles at the centre, e.g. the degrees at the interior angles of an octagon are calculated as follows:

$$\frac{(2 \times 8) - 4}{8} \times 90 = 135 \text{ degs.}$$

Regular Polygons

There are various ways of drawing regular polygons. Fig. 34 shows a method of drawing the hexagon. A circle of radius equal to the length of one side of the required figure is described, and the length of the radius is plotted around the circumference; it goes exactly six times and by joining the points so obtained the figure is completed. It will be seen that the hexagon contains six equilateral triangles.

Fig. 35 shows an alternative method of drawing the same figure. A base line AB, equal to the length of one side, is drawn; using a 60-degree set-square, lines are drawn in two directions from A and B; from the intersection R of the two inner lines a horizontal line is drawn to terminate the other two lines at C and D. This gives half the required figure, which is completed by continuing lines AR and BR, and by drawing lines at 60 degrees from C and D as shown.

Fig. 36 shows the construction of a regular octagon within an enclosing square $ABCD$. The diagonals of the square are drawn; then, with radius equal to half the length of a diagonal and centres A, B, C, D in turn arcs are drawn as indicated giving points of intersection on the sides of the square, which when joined give the required octagon. It will be seen that an octagon contains eight isosceles triangles.

Fig. 37 shows the construction of an octagon with sides of given length by using the tee-square and 45-degree set-square.

To Construct any Regular Polygon

Any regular polygon can be drawn by dividing the circumference of a circle into a number of equal parts corresponding to the number of sides of the required polygon, and then by joining the points.

A method of drawing a polygon within a given circle is shown in Fig. 38. The circle is drawn with diameter AB. With centre A and any radius a semi-circle is drawn. This semi-circle is divided into as many parts as the required polygon is to have sides, say five. From A radials are drawn through the points on the semi-circle cutting the circle in points which are the angles of the required figure, in this case a pentagon.

Fig. 39 shows the method of construction which can be applied to any regular polygon when the length of one side AB is known. AB is produced, and with B as centre and any radius a semi-circle CDE is described. This semi-circle is divided by trial into the same number of parts as the required polygon is to have sides, say seven. Through division 2 on the semi-circle a line BF is drawn equal to AB. BF and AB are bisected and the bisectors produced to meet in O. With centre O and radius OA a circle

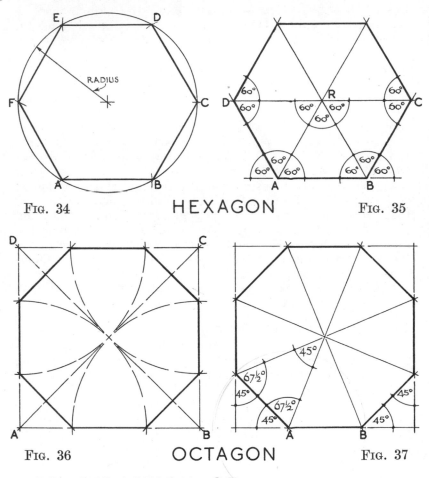

FIG. 34   **HEXAGON**   FIG. 35

FIG. 36   **OCTAGON**   FIG. 37

**CONSTRUCTION OF
REGULAR POLYGONS**

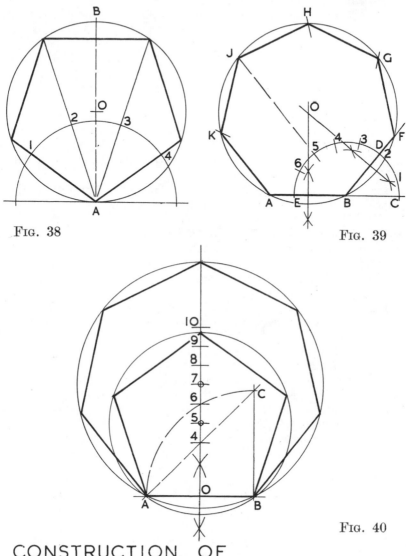

Fig. 38

Fig. 39

Fig. 40

CONSTRUCTION OF
REGULAR POLYGONS

is described and points G, H, K marked on its circumference so that AG, GH, HJ, JK equal AB; by joining these points the figure is completed.

Fig. 40 shows another method of drawing a regular polygon on a given straight line AB. At B a perpendicular BC is drawn equal to AB and C is joined to A. AB is bisected in O and a perpendicular of indefinite length is erected cutting AC in 4 (4 is the centre of a square raised on AB). With B as centre a quadrant is drawn $A6C$; then 6 is the centre of a hexagon described on AB. Midway between 4 and 6, point 5 is the centre of a pentagon described on AB. If points 7, 8, 9, etc., are marked on the perpendicular from 0 so that the divisions are equal to 4–5 or 5–6, then these points are the centres of other regular polygons described on AB with sides equal in number to the index figure.

(Note: It is only possible to produce satisfactory results by the above methods by careful and accurate drawing.)

Use of Irregular Polygons in Surveying

Irregular polygons are used chiefly in surveying practice. Field surveying using the chain, plane table and box sextant has been briefly dealt with in previous pages; the use of the theodolite is referred to in the following description.

Fig. 41 shows the method of surveying an irregular field of, say, seven sides. The angles of the field are picketed off with ranging poles at stations A, B, C D, E, F, G. Firstly, the distances between the various stations are carefully measured and recorded in the field book. Should it be possible, although it rarely is the case, the theodolite is then levelled up in a favourable position in the field so that all stations are visible for taking readings. It is usual, however, to commence at station A, moving round to B, C, D, etc., obtaining the measurement in degrees of the internal angles, known as making a Theodolite Traverse Survey. To obtain a check on the work, it is necessary to traverse round and back to the starting-point, i.e. making a "closed" traverse. The theodolite is normally read using the compass so that the bearing of each line in relation to the points of the compass, i.e. the "magnetic bearing" of each line, is determined.

In Figs. 41–42 the polygonal boundary of the field with the measured internal angles is shown, together with the field book entries. The survey can be checked for accuracy of angle measurement by applying the rule respecting angles of any polygon previously mentioned.

Frequently, in the drawing of an irregular polygon as described above, the figure fails to close because of faulty observations,

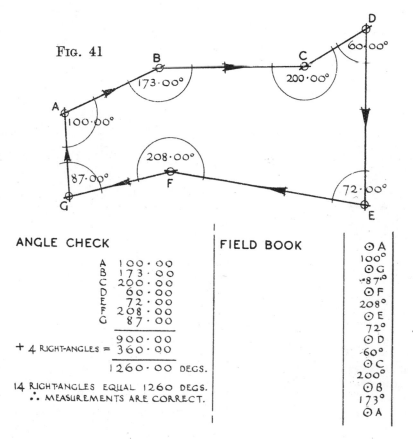

FIG. 41

ANGLE CHECK | FIELD BOOK

⊙ A
100°
⊙ G
-87°
⊙ F
208°
⊙ E
72°
⊙ D
60°
⊙ C
200°
⊙ B
173°
⊙ A

A	100 · 00
B	173 · 00
C	200 · 00
D	60 · 00
E	72 · 00
F	208 · 00
G	87 · 00

900 · 00
+ 4 RIGHT-ANGLES = 360 · 00

1260 · 00 DEGS.

14 RIGHT-ANGLES EQUAL 1260 DEGS.
∴ MEASUREMENTS ARE CORRECT.

FIG. 42

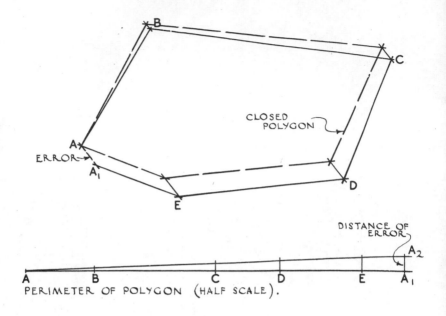

FIG. 43

inaccurate measuring or setting out. In Fig. 43 an error $A-A_1$ is indicated. To adjust this, the perimeter of the polygon is drawn out as a straight line $ABCDEA_1$, as shown—this may have to be done to scale to avoid undue length. At A_1 on the developed perimeter a perpendicular is erected, and made the same distance as the error, A_1A_2. A_2 is joined to A, and perpendiculars cutting A_2A are erected from points B, C, D, E. These perpendiculars show the proportionate amount of error to be allowed for at each angle of the polygon. On the original survey, plotting lines are drawn from each angle parallel to the line of error $A-A_1$, and by marking off on these parallels the respective proportions of error as determined above, and by joining the points so obtained the polygon is replotted and will now close.

CHAPTER IV

CIRCLES

THE circle is a plane figure confined by a curved line known as the *circumference*, all points on which are equidistant from a point known as the *centre* of the circle. Fig. 44 shows circles illustrating the terms defined below:

Arc—A part of the circumference.

Chord—A straight line, shorter than the diameter, terminated by the circumference at both ends.

Diameter—A straight line passing through the centre of the circle and terminated at both ends by the circumference.

Normal—A straight line drawn from any point on the circumference radial to the centre of the circle.

Quadrant—A quarter of a circle in shape and area.

Radius—A straight line drawn from the centre of a circle to the circumference (plural—*radii*).

Sector—A part of a circle contained between two radii which form an angle of less than 180 degrees.

Semi-circle—A half circle in shape and area; the part on either side of a diameter.

Segment—A part of a circle contained between a chord and its arc.

Tangent—A straight line touching the circumference of a circle at one point at right-angles to a normal at that point.

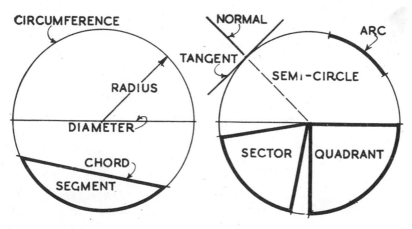

FIG. 44

33

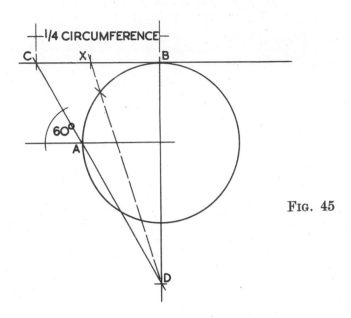

Fig. 45

The Circumference

The circumference of a circle is approximately 3·141 or $3\frac{1}{7}$ times the diameter in length. $3\frac{1}{7}$ is usually expressed by the Greek letter π and the formula for the length of the circumference as $\pi \times D$. For example: the circumference of a 3″ diameter circle is $\pi \times D = 3\cdot141 \times 3 = 9\cdot423$ inches.

Fig. 45 shows a useful practical method of finding the length of a $\frac{1}{4}$ circumference or smaller segment. A line is drawn from A at 60 degrees to the horizontal to cut the tangent at B produced at C. BC is then the developed $\frac{1}{4}$ circumference. By drawing a perpendicular line from B to meet CA produced a point D is found, from which lines can be drawn through any point on the $\frac{1}{4}$ circumference AB to the line CB to give the development of the arcs.

(Note: Although very slightly inaccurate, this method is satisfactory for most practical purposes.)

In geometrical drawing it is common practice to find the development of the circumference of a circle by dividing it into a number of equal units which can be plotted on a straight line. This method is not, of course, accurate, as the plotted units, however small, are chords of the circle.

The Area of a Circle

The area of a circle is found from the mathematical formula—
$\pi \times \text{radius}^2$.

For example: the area of a 3″ diameter circle is $3 \cdot 14 \times 1 \cdot 5^2 = 7 \cdot 06$ square inches.

To Find the Radius of a Segment

The mathematical formula for finding the radius of a segment of a circle, the chord and rise being known, is—

$$\text{radius} = \frac{(\frac{1}{2} \text{ chord})^2 + (\text{rise})^2}{2 \text{ rise}}.$$

A practical application of this arises in the setting out of a segmental wall, the chord of which is, say, 14′ 0″ and the rise, say, 3′ 0″. The radius to be marked off on a batten or lath to be used for describing the curve will be:

$$\frac{(\frac{1}{2} 14)^2 + 3^2}{2 \times 3} = \frac{7^2 + 3^2}{6} = \frac{58}{6} = 9' \; 8''.$$

Segmental Arches

There are various methods of finding the shapes of turning pieces, shaped lintels, wood centres, etc., for segmental arches. Fig. 46 illustrates the method of finding the curve of the soffit of a segmental arch, the span of which is AC and the rise DB. With compasses AB and BC are bisected. The intersection of the bisecting lines, O, is the centre for striking the required arc. Although this method can be used in practice it is more suitable for drawing plans, etc.

A more practical method is shown in Fig. 47. Taking an arch of similar proportions to the foregoing, pieces of thin batten are formed into a triangle of the form of the triangle ABC, as illustrated—or, if the arch is flat enough, a single wide board can be so shaped. Nails are fixed at points A and C on the timber to be cut, and with a pencil held at the apex B of the triangle the required curve can be drawn by moving the triangle, keeping the sides against the nails, as shown.

Problems Relating to Circles

Fig. 48 shows the method of describing a circle to pass through three points, A, B and C. AB and BC are bisected; where the bisectors intersect at O is the centre of the required circle.

Fig. 49 illustrates how continuous arcs can be drawn to pass through a series of points, 1, 2, 3, 4 and 5. The method is based on the previous example. It will be seen that the centres of the

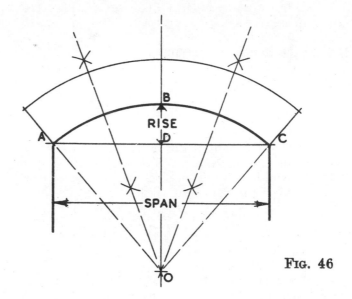

B

RISE

A   D   C

SPAN

O

Fig. 46

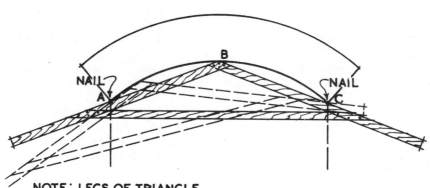

B

NAIL   NAIL
A   C

NOTE: LEGS OF TRIANGLE
TO BE LONG ENOUGH TO
COMPLETE ARC REQUIRED

Fig. 47

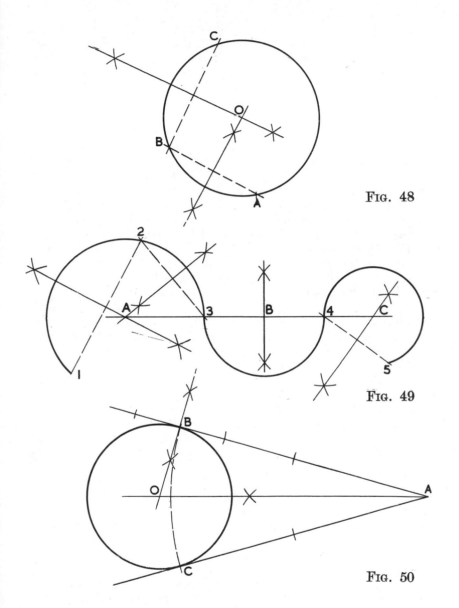

FIG. 48

FIG. 49

FIG. 50

arcs lie on a normal common to all arcs. In forming continuous curves of arcs the centres A, B and C, of adjoining arcs must have a common normal.

Fig. 50 shows how a circle is described within an angle BAC. The circle is tangential at points B and C, which are equidistant from A. Using compasses a line is drawn at right-angles to BA at B, and the angle BAC is bisected. The intersection of the line and the bisector gives a point O which is the centre of the required circle.

Fig. 51 shows the method of drawing a series of circles tangential to each other and to be tangential to two converging lines AB and AC. The angle formed by the converging lines BAC is bisected and the first circle with centre O is drawn by the method described in the previous example. The angle FOE is bisected, the bisector cutting AC at G. With centre G and radius GF an arc is described to cut AC at H. By drawing from H parallel to FO the centre of the next circle is found along AD, and the method can be repeated for other circles as required.

Fig. 52 shows how six small equal circles can be drawn to connect a series of circular arcs meeting at a common centre. The latter are drawn by dividing up the circumference of a larger circle into six equal parts indicated by the figures 1, 2, 3, 4, 5 and 6, which are the centres for the arcs, the radius being equal to that of the circle. A line is then drawn from point 2 through point 1. At 1 a semi-circle of radius equal to that of the required smaller circles is drawn, giving points A and B on the line 2.1. With centre 1 and radius $2B$ and centre 2 and radius $2A$ arcs are drawn to intersect at C, which is the centre for a smaller circle connecting the arcs $O6$ and $O1$. The centres of the other smaller circles can be similarly found.

Fig. 53 shows how two circles can be drawn tangential to each other and to the arc of a greater circle of given radius. A line AB is drawn equal to the combined length of the diameters of the two circles. The radii of the circles are then marked off from A and B respectively to find the centres C and D, around which the circles are described. Having a common normal they are tangential. To find the centre of the greater circle, its radius OP is marked off from A and B, giving AF and BE equal to OP. With centres C and D and radii CF and DE respectively arcs are described intersecting at O which is the centre of the required circle.

Fig. 54 shows three equal tangential circles inscribed within two equal arcs (e.g. main lines of tracery in a pointed arch). An equilateral triangle ABC is first drawn and three circles are then described with centres A, B and C and radius equal to half the length of the sides of the triangle. A horizontal line is then drawn

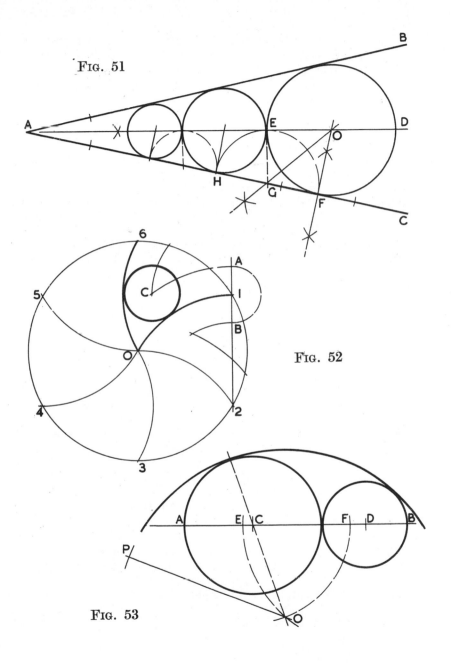

FIG. 51

FIG. 52

FIG. 53

tangential to two of the circles, as shown, and the intersections of this line and the bisectors of angles BAC and ACB give points 1 and 2 which are the centres for the required arcs.

Fig. 55 shows the method of inscribing eight equal tangential circles within an octagon. The octagon is divided into its eight isosceles triangles. In one of these AOB the angles ABO and BOA are bisected; the intersection of the bisectors gives the centre C of one of the required circles, the radius being CD. The other circles can then be plotted.

Fig. 56 shows a regular hexagon with six equal tangential inscribed circles. The method is similar to that used in the previous example.

Fig. 57 illustrates the method of drawing the outline of an ogee (double curve) dome or arch. The span and height being determined, a line AB is drawn from the springing to the apex. A point C is marked along this line where it is desired the curve should change direction, and AC and CB are bisected. The intersections of the bisectors with horizontal lines drawn through A and B, as shown, give the centres (1 and 2) for the required arcs for one side of the dome or arch. The centres for drawing the other side can be plotted as shown by the broken lines.

Fig. 58 shows the setting out of the outline for a W.C. seat. AB, the width, is bisected at C and a circle with centre C and radius equal to AC is described. Lines are then drawn from A and B through D, the point where the circle is cut by the perpendicular bisector of AB. A, B and D are then used as centres for arcs to complete the figure as shown.

Fig. 59 shows the setting out of the outline of an egg-shaped sewer. The method is similar to that of the foregoing. FA is equal to half AB, and FE is equal to twice AB.

Fig. 60 shows the setting out of the section of a handrail. An equilateral triangle ABC, is constructed with sides equal to the width of the handrail, and a rectangle, $ABED$, is constructed on AB which is then divided into 5 equal parts. Lines are drawn from one division from A and B to D and E respectively. Where these lines, $1D$ and $4E$, intersect AC and BC, centres are found at F and G for the construction of arcs as continuations of an arc described with centre C. The section is then completed by further arcs of radius equal to those struck from F and G but with centres at H and K, and straight lines as shown.

Fig. 61 is a drawing of a typical standard steel beam section—$10'' \times 5''$ Rolled Steel Joist—showing the use of arcs in its setting out.

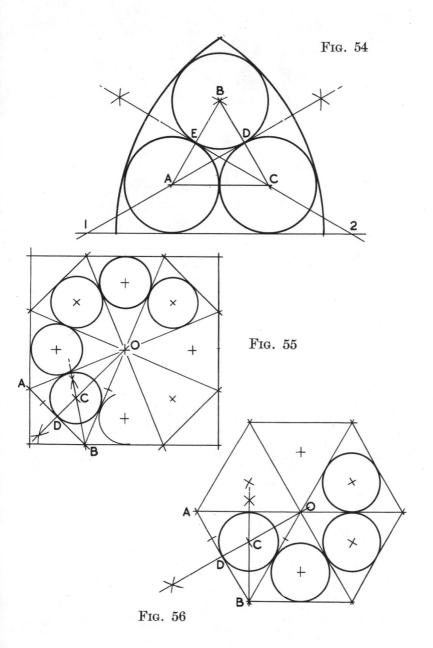

FIG. 54

FIG. 55

FIG. 56

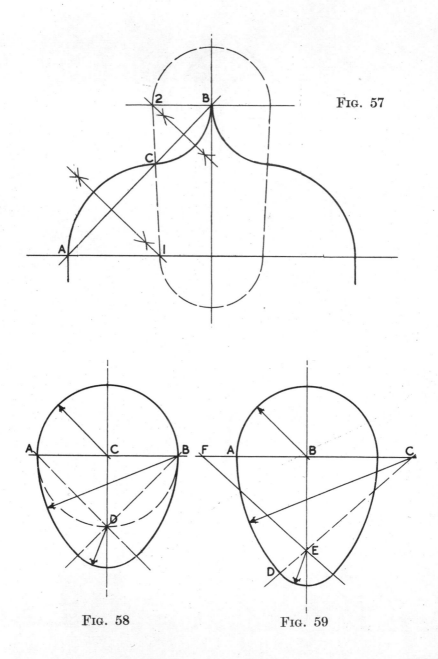

FIG. 57

FIG. 58   FIG. 59

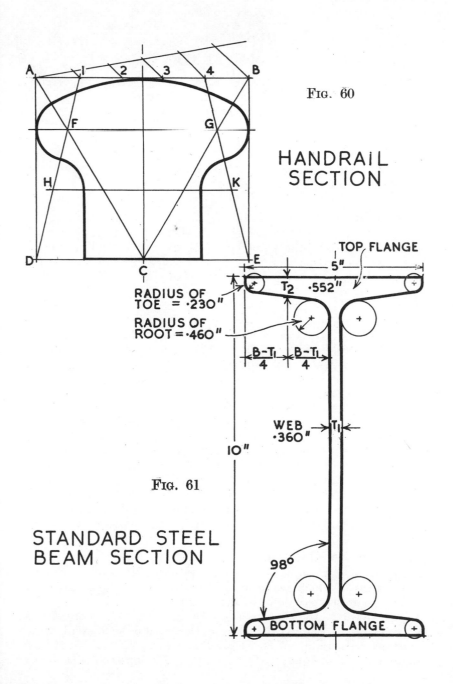

FIG. 60

HANDRAIL
SECTION

TOP FLANGE

5"

T_2 ·552"

RADIUS OF
TOE = ·230"

RADIUS OF
ROOT = ·460"

$\dfrac{B-T_1}{4}$ $\dfrac{B-T_1}{4}$

WEB
·360" T_1

10"

FIG. 61

STANDARD STEEL
BEAM SECTION

98°

BOTTOM FLANGE

CHAPTER V
SPIRAL CURVES

ARCHIMEDEAN SPIRAL; SPIRALS BASED ON QUADRANTS; SETTING
OUT OF VOLUTE FOR IONIC CAPITAL, CURTAIL STEPS, ETC.

A SPIRAL curve is the locus of a point moving on a plane surface
about a fixed point in such a way as to approach nearer to or
recede farther from the fixed point in a regular manner.

Of the various spiral curves the following examples have been
chosen as being of the greatest practical value.

Archimedean or Equable Spiral

Fig. 62 illustrates the principle of this curve. A is the fixed
point or centre of the spiral and $A1$ the longest radius vector
(i.e. the line from the fixed point to the farthest point of the
locus). Lines $A2$, $A3$, $A4$, $A5$ are drawn, the angles formed at
A being all equal. $A1$ is divided into 10 (or any number) equal
parts and using compasses with centre A points are marked on
$A1$, $A2$, $A3$, etc., at progressively shorter distances by one
division from A. A free curve passing through these points is
part of the required spiral curve. The name "equable" applied
to this curve is self-explanatory; "Archimedean" is after Archi-
medes, a mathematician of Ancient Greece, who made much use
of the properties of the spiral.

Fig. 63 illustrates the construction of an Archimedean spiral
of two convolutions, i.e. one in which the moving point travels
twice round the fixed point. OA is the longest radius vector and
is divided into 24 parts. Other radius vectors are drawn so that
twelve equal angular spaces are formed. Then, using compasses
with centre O and radii progressively shorter by one division from
A arcs are drawn to cut the vectors in turn. By joining the points
so obtained in a smooth curve the required spiral is drawn.

(Note: Great care is required in drawing these freehand curves.)

Spirals based on Quadrants

Fig. 64 shows a spiral of constant pitch built up of quadrants,
the centres of which are located at the corners of a square. The
pitch equals the perimeter of the square.

Fig. 65 shows the construction of the outline of the tread of a
curtail step. Assuming the width of the tread to be 9″, a quadrant
is drawn with radius of half that distance, i.e. $4\frac{1}{2}″$, which is then
divided into four equal parts, and a square is constructed at index

EQUABLE
SPIRALS

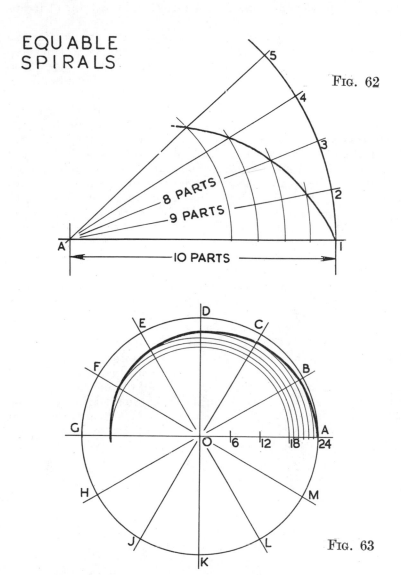

F<small>IG</small>. 62

A

8 PARTS

9 PARTS

I

⟵ IO PARTS ⟶

F<small>IG</small>. 63

point 4 with sides equal to one of these divisions. The perimeter of the square is thus equal to $4\frac{1}{2}''$. Quadrants drawn with centres at the corners of the square enable the curve of the step to be completed, as shown, using D as centre for a quadrant of radius equal to the quadrant struck from C.

Fig. 66 shows the method of setting out the templet for the built-up block and tread of a curtail step. The width of the step from riser to riser is divided into seven equal parts. A horizontal line 08 is drawn equal in length to eight of these units. With centre 0 and radius 01 an arc is described and from 8 a line is drawn tangential to it. With centre 4 and radius the greatest distance from 4 to this line an arc is described to cut 08 at A. With centre A and radius $A8$ a quadrant arc $A8G$ is drawn. From G a line is drawn at right-angles to the tangent line, and from the point of intersection a line is drawn to A and another line at right-angles to it also passing through the point of inter-section as shown. It is then possible to plot the points B, C, D, E, which are the centres for successive quadrants to form the required curve. Centre A and radius $A6$ are used in describing the curve to complete the shape of the step.

There are many methods of setting out the characteristic spiral scroll or volute of the capital of the Ionic order in Architecture, illustrated in Fig. 67. Some of them, particularly Greek examples, are very complex; they can be found in standard works on the Orders in most reference libraries

Fig. 68 shows a comparatively simple setting out from the works of Vignola, a famous architect of the Italian Renaissance. The line 08 in the figure represents the required overall vertical dimension of the volute. The unit 34 is the diameter of the "eye" and fixes its position. The enlarged detail of this "eye" shows how the centres for the arcs forming the curve are arranged. The centres for the outer spiral are numbered 1–12 and are equal divisions along the diagonals. The centres for the inner spiral are one-third of a division in from the numbered points.

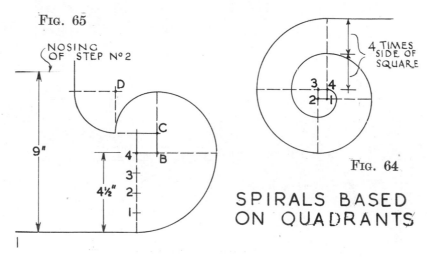

FIG. 65

NOSING
OF STEP N⁰ 2

D

C

9"

4 | B

3

4½" 2

1

4 TIMES
SIDE OF
SQUARE

3 4

2 1

FIG. 64

SPIRALS BASED
ON QUADRANTS

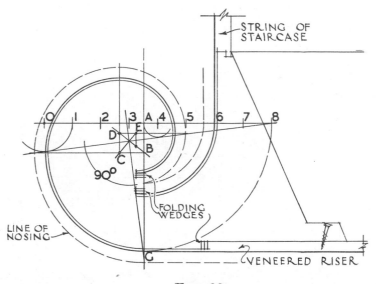

STRING OF
STAIRCASE

0 1 2 3 A 4 5 6 7 8

D E

B

C

90°

FOLDING
WEDGES

LINE OF
NOSING

G

VENEERED RISER

FIG. 66

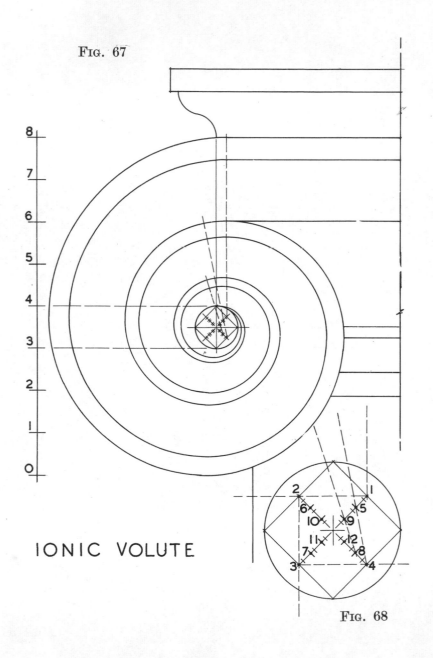

Fig. 67

8
7
6
5
4
3
2
1
0

IONIC VOLUTE

2   1
6   5
10   9
11   12
7   8
3   4

Fig. 68

CHAPTER VI
PLANE CURVES

THE ELLIPSE; PSEUDO-ELLIPTICAL ARCH; 3-CENTRE ARCH;
5-CENTRE ARCH; THE PARABOLA; THE HYPERBOLA; OUTLINES
OF ARCHES

The Ellipse

Considered as a plane curve, the ellipse is the locus of a point tracing a continuous curve in such a way that the sum of the distances from the point to two fixed points or foci is always constant.

When a cone or cylinder is cut by an inclined plane the outline of the section obtained is an ellipse—as shown in Fig. 69.

The curve of the ellipse in whole or part is considerably used in building design, and a knowledge of its setting out and its properties is essential to the draughtsman and the practical man.

There are many methods of setting out the ellipse; the more important for various purposes are given below.

Trammel Method of Setting Out Ellipses

This is suitable for almost all purposes. Fig. 70 illustrates the application to drawing. The lengths of the major axis AB and the minor axis CD having been determined and drawn at right-angles to one another so that they intersect at O midway along each axis, a straight strip of stout paper (the Trammel) is taken and a distance equal to half the major axis is marked on it, and within this distance half the minor axis, CO, is also marked off from one end. By placing the strip of paper on the drawing so that the two marks separated by the difference between the distances fall on the axes as shown, and then by moving the paper, but always keeping the marks on the axes, the third mark can be made to trace the curve of the ellipse.

Fig. 71 shows how the method can be applied for marking out an ellipse on, for example, a plot of land, using grooved planks in the directions of the major and minor axes, and with a batten as trammel arranged to slide in them.

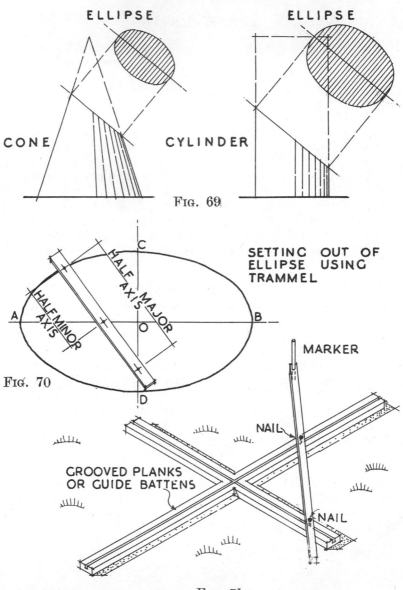

ELLIPSE

ELLIPSE

CONE

CYLINDER

FIG. 69

C

HALF MAJOR AXIS

HALF MINOR AXIS

A

O

B

SETTING OUT OF
ELLIPSE USING
TRAMMEL

FIG. 70

D

MARKER

NAIL

GROOVED PLANKS
OR GUIDE BATTENS

NAIL

FIG. 71

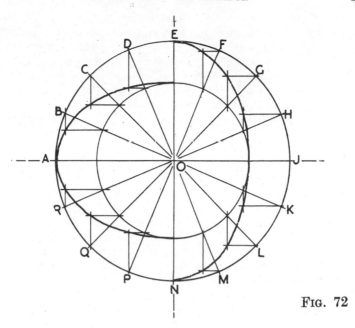

FIG. 72

Other Methods of Setting Out the Ellipse

Fig, 72 shows the setting out by means of two circles with common centre O and diameters equal to the major and minor axes. Any convenient number of radials are drawn cutting both circles and from the points so obtained lines parallel to the axes are drawn. The intersections of these lines give points on the curve of the ellipse.

Fig. 73 illustrates a similar method. The axes, AB and CD, and the foci, F and F^1, are given. The distance between the foci is divided into an odd number of units—in the example seven are shown—which are indexed. Then the procedure is to take compasses and with radius equal to $A1$ and with F^1 as centre to describe an arc, and with radius equal to $B1$ and centre F to describe another arc to cut the first one. Similarly with radii equal to $A2$ and $B2$, and so on as shown. The intersections of the arcs give points on the curve which can then be drawn.

In Fig. 74 the major and minor axes, AB and CD, having been drawn, the foci are found by using compasses and with radius equal to AO and with centre C by cutting the major axis at F and F^1. Assuming the ellipse is being drawn on a piece of plywood, then nails are fixed at F, F^1 and C and a length of string is fastened to F and F^1 and passed tightly round C. By releasing the nail at C and putting a pencil in the loop the curve can be drawn by moving the pencil around the foci, keeping it tightly against the string.

Fig. 75 shows the construction of an ellipse within a rectangle. The rectangle $EFGH$ is drawn about the major and minor axes, AB and CD, as shown. AE and EC are both divided into the same number of equal parts, which are indexed. Then by drawing from A to the division points marked on EC and from C to the division points marked on AE intersections are made through which a quarter of the curve of the ellipse can be drawn. The procedure is repeated in the remaining parts of the rectangle.

Fig. 76 illustrates an alternative method of drawing an ellipse in a rectangle. The method is somewhat similar to the foregoing and can be understood from the diagram. The segment of an ellipse can also be drawn in the same way as shown in Fig. 77, in which DC represents the major or minor axis and $AEFB$ the rectangle in which the segment is to be drawn. The same principle can be again employed in setting out a rampant or raking ellipse, as shown in Fig. 78, or alternatively, the method illustrated in Fig. 75 can be employed.

Pseudo-Elliptical Arches

Arches of true semi-elliptical curve are seldom used in masonry and brick construction owing to the expense of cutting the stones or gauged bricks, and curves made up of arcs approximating to a semi-ellipse are used. Two types are described below.

3-Centred Arch

Fig. 79 illustrates a 3-centred elliptical arch in masonry. AB is the clear span which is divided into four equal parts to find centres 1 and 2. From these centres tangent circles are described. From each circle tangent lines at 45 degrees to the horizontal are drawn to intersect and so give centre 3. With centre 3 and radius extended to become tangent to the circles an arc can be drawn to complete the arch. Note the radiating of the joint lines from centres 1, 2 and 3.

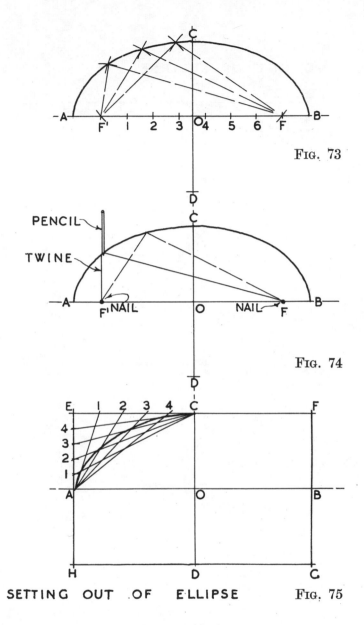

FIG. 73

PENCIL

TWINE

F'NAIL   O   NAIL F

FIG. 74

SETTING OUT OF ELLIPSE   FIG. 75

SETTING OUT OF ELLIPSE

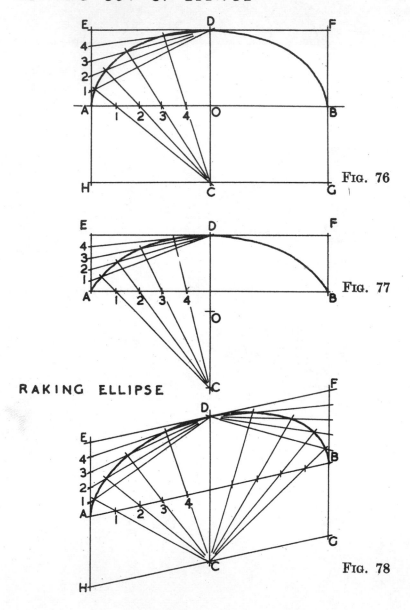

FIG. 76

FIG. 77

RAKING ELLIPSE

FIG. 78

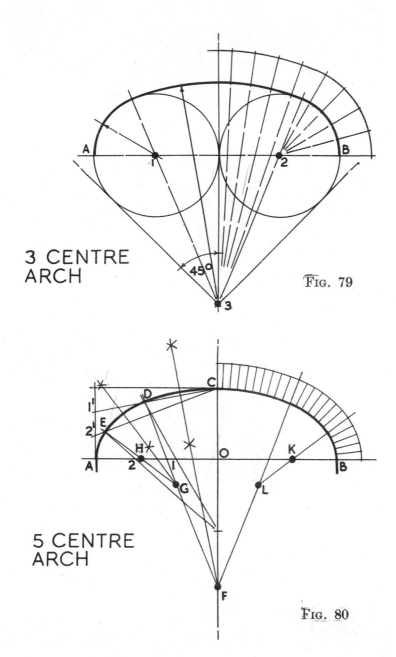

3 CENTRE ARCH

45°

FIG. 79

5 CENTRE ARCH

FIG. 80

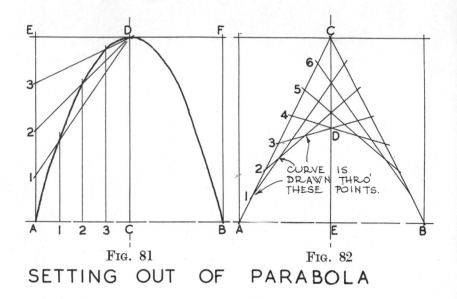

Fig. 81

Fig. 82

SETTING OUT OF PARABOLA

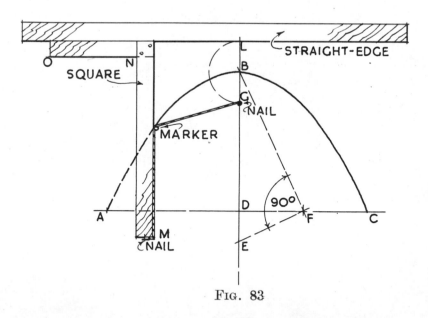

Fig. 83

5-Centred Arch

This more nearly approximates to a true semi-ellipse. In Fig. 80 the method is shown applied to the formation of a gauged brick arch, there being three sets of bricks for the five segments of the arch. AB is the clear span of the arch and OC is the rise. AO is divided into three equal parts, and the divisions are indexed 1 and 2. At A a perpendicular is drawn equal to OC and is also divided into three equal parts, the divisions being indexed 1^1 and 2^1. From a point along the vertical axis at a distance from O equal to OC, lines are drawn through 1 and 2 to contact corresponding lines drawn from C to 1^1 and 2^1, giving points D and E. DC is bisected and the bisector is produced to cut the vertical axis at F. F is joined to D. DE is bisected and the bisector is produced to cut DF at G. G is joined to E, cutting AO at H. Points K and L are plotted on the other side of the vertical axis to correspond to H and G. F, H, G, K, L are then the five centres for drawing the arcs to complete the curve.

THE PARABOLA

This curve is the outline of the section obtained when a cone is cut parallel to its inclination. It is the curve which a suspended cable assumes; the curve of a bending moment diagram for an evenly distributed load in structural calculations; and is the most static arch form. The curve is widely used in design because of its properties in reflecting sound, light and heat.

Setting Out the Parabola

Fig. 81 shows a method of drawing a parabola. AB is the width or base line and CD the height of the curve. On AB a rectangle $AEFB$ is constructed, the height being equal to CD. AE is divided into a number of equal parts and AC is divided into the same number of parts. Lines are drawn from the points of division on AE to D, and from the points on AC perpendicular are erected. Where intersections are made points, as shown, through which one half of the curve can be drawn are found. The procedure is repeated to complete the whole curve.

Fig. 82 shows the method of drawing a parabola when the axis, height and ordinates are given. AB is the ordinate, EC the axis and D the vertex or point where the curve cuts the axis. DC is made equal to ED. Lines AC and CB are drawn and each divided into the same number of units, and the points of division are indexed as shown. By joining corresponding divisions intersections are made through which the curve can be drawn.

The foregoing methods can be used in drawing rampant para-
bolas in a similar manner to the drawing of rampant ellipses
previously described.

Describing a Parabola for Practical Work

Fig. 83 shows how a parabola can be set out for practical work
using a straight-edge and square. AC is the ordinate and DB
the axis; B is the vertex. DC is bisected in F, which is joined
to B. FE is drawn at right-angles to BF to cut the axis BD
produced in E. BG is set off equal to DE and G is the focal point
of the parabola. BL is made equal to BG and the straight-edge
is laid on L parallel to AC. A piece of string equal in length to
LE is attached at one end to a nail at G and at the other end
to M on the square MNO. By sliding the square along the
straight-edge and at the same time keeping the string tight against
the square with a pencil or marker the curve can be drawn.

THE HYPERBOLA

This curve is the outline of the section obtained when a cone
is cut perpendicular to its base, but not through the centre of
the base.

Setting out the Hyperbola

Fig. 84 shows a method of drawing a hyperbola when the
axis, CG, the vertex, D, and the ordinate, AC, are given. On
AC a rectangle, $ACDE$, is constructed. AC and AE are then
divided into a convenient number of corresponding parts. From
the divisions along AC lines are drawn to G, and from the corresponding divisions along AE lines are drawn to D. Where intersections are made points are found through which one-half the
required curve can be drawn as shown. The procedure can then
be repeated to complete the whole curve.

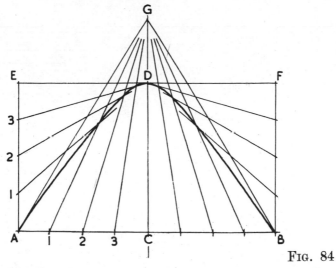

FIG. 84

SETTING OUT OF HYPERBOLA

Arches

Fig. 85 illustrates further examples of the setting out of arches —the Flat or Camber "arch," the Semi-circular and Segmental arches, commonly used in brickwork; and the Lancet, Equilateral and Four-Centre pointed arches.

There are various other forms of the arch, but as they are not in common use and do not present any special problems in setting out they are not included here.

The detail drawings of the Circular opening formed with axed (shaped) bricks and the Segmental two-ring rough brick arch illustrate the characteristic differences in setting out the bricks.

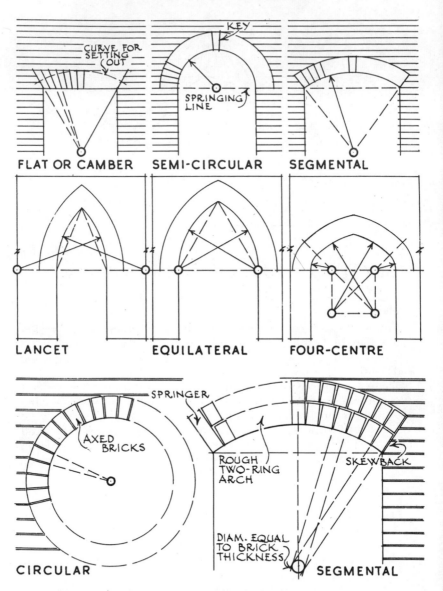

SETTING OUT OF ARCHES

Fig. 85

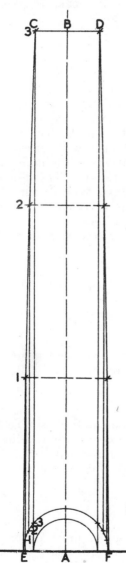

SETTING OUT
OF ENTASIS

FIG. 86

CHAPTER VII

ENTASIS

ENTASIS is the swelling or curving outwards along the outline of a column shaft intended to counteract the optical illusion which gives a tapering shaft bounded by straight lines the appearance of curving inwards, and, as used by the Classical Greeks, to convey a subtle impression of the weight-bearing function of the column.

Method of Setting out Entasis

There are various methods, some giving an unpleasant exaggerated curve, but the one usually employed is illustrated in Fig. 86. AB is the height of the shaft and CD and EF the top and bottom diameters respectively. With centre A and radii AE and BC two semi-circles are drawn as shown. A perpendicular is erected from the limit of the smaller semi-circle to cut the larger semi-circle in 3. The segment $E3$ is divided into any number of equal parts—say three—and indexed from A. Through points 1 and 2 perpendiculars are erected to cut corresponding divisions in the height of the shaft. Through the points so obtained the required curve from E to C is drawn. The other side is drawn similarly.

A variation of this method is to draw the sides of the shaft perpendicular from the lower diameter for one-third the height and then to proceed by the method described above.

CHAPTER VIII
GEOMETRICAL DECORATION

CONTINUOUS BAND AND REPEATING PATTERNS; PATTERNS FILLING
ENCLOSED AREAS. TRACERY

DECORATIVE designs used for all manner of purposes are frequently set out on a geometrical basis and sometimes consist
entirely of combinations of straight and curved lines forming
elementary figures of plane geometry. Generally, such geometrical designs should be developed out of the functional or
structural requirements of the building or object concerned—e.g.
the diaper and other patterns which result from the bonding of
brickwork—and should not be arbitrarily applied without careful
consideration of the possibilities and limitations of the materials
used, including the effects of colour, texture, etc. The designs
shown here, therefore, are intended to illustrate typical examples
only of geometrical pattern and ornament—variations of which
are limitless—and their main constructional lines.

There are many types of designs but they can be grouped as
follows:

1. Continuous and Ribbon-like Bands.
2. Repeating or All-over Patterns, which can be extended in
   any direction.
3. Patterns filling Regular Enclosed Areas.
4. Tracery.

Detailed descriptions of the construction is not given below as
they have been covered in the foregoing chapters.

Continuous and Ribbon-like Bands

Fig. 87. A, B and C show the development from simple to
more complex patterns, employing horizontal and vertical lines,
diagonals, and circles. Actual examples are illustrated in Fig. 88,
D and E: a wrought metal railing (modern Danish), and a metal
staircase balustrade (modern Swedish).

Repeating Patterns

Fig. 89. A, B, C, D, E and F show various examples of simple
repeating patterns built up from squares and circles. Actual
examples, Fig. 90, G and H, are: a coffered ceiling in plaster
(modern Swedish) and a floor pattern (Spanish Saracenic).

FIG. 87

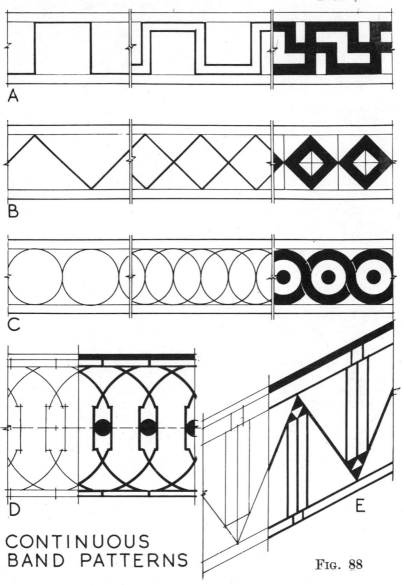

A

B

C

D

CONTINUOUS
BAND PATTERNS

E

FIG. 88

Regular Areas

In designing a geometrical pattern to fill a regular area, atten-
tion should be paid to the axes, forms and lines suggested by its
shape. The squares in Fig. 91 have patterns based on: A—concentric squares, B—concentric squares and diagonals, C—a star,
D—circles.

Patterns to fill circles are usually based on concentric rings or
radial lines or on a combination of these. Fig. 92 E and F show
a concentric pattern (actual example—coloured marble wall
decoration, Pisa Cathedral) and a radial pattern.

Similar designs are possible within other regular geometrical
figures.

Tracery

All Gothic window tracery is based on geometrical setting out
to some degree, and during an early phase of its development
elementary geometrical shapes were much used, hence the name
Geometrical Tracery.

Fig. 93, A, B, C and D show methods of filling small circular
windows with tracery (the patterns are of course adaptable to
other types of decoration) and E is a typical example of an
"Early English" Gothic window head from a parish church in
Kent.

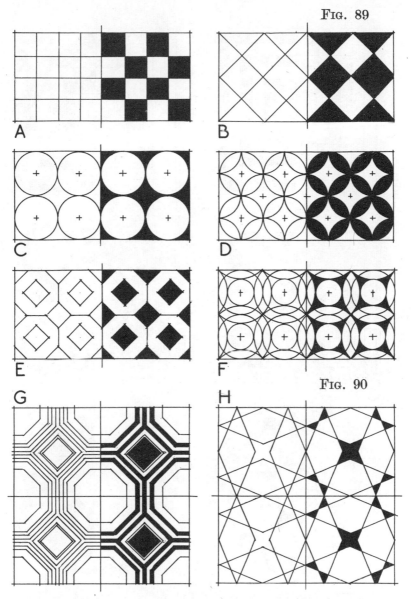

FIG. 89

FIG. 90

REPEATING ALL-OVER PATTERNS

FIG. 91

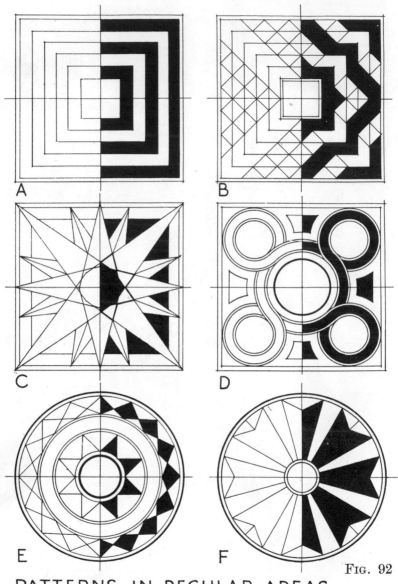

A

B

C

D

E

F

FIG. 92

PATTERNS IN REGULAR AREAS

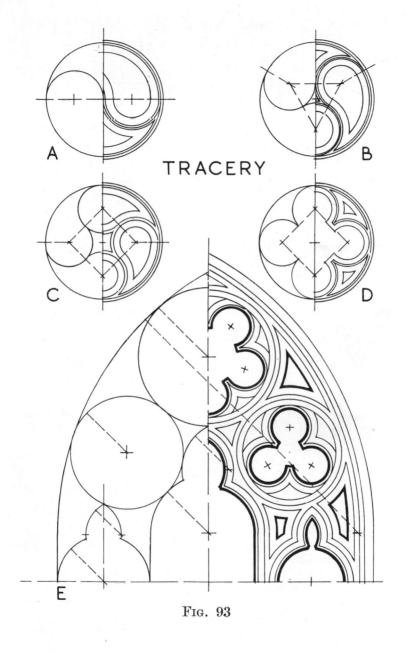

TRACERY

A

B

C

D

E

FIG. 93

SOLID GEOMETRY

CHAPTER IX
ORTHOGRAPHIC PROJECTION

PLANS, ELEVATIONS AND SECTIONS. ISOMETRIC, AXONOMETRIC
AND OBLIQUE PROJECTION

Orthographic Projection

THE usual method of showing designs of buildings or solid objects
(which are actually three-dimensional) in two-dimensional scale
drawings is by means of related views termed plans, elevations
and sections.

Plan—a view of a building or object represented on a horizontal
plane.

Elevation—a view of a building or object represented on a
vertical plane.

Section—a view of a building or object obtained by making an
imaginary cut through it usually in a vertical plane
on which it is represented. (Note: A horizontal cut
gives what is correctly known as a sectional plan, but
what is usually included in the general classification
of plans.)

These terms will be more readily understood by reference to
Fig. 94, which shows a box drawn in plan, elevation and section.
In making the drawing, the elevation is projected from the plan,
and the section from the elevation and plan by means of projectors
or construction lines which determine the salient points.

According to the design of the building or object, several plans,
elevations and sections may be required to show it fully. It is
usual in drawing a building, for example, in this way to show a
plan (sectional plan) through each floor as well as of the roof and
foundations, elevations of all sides, and a number of sections
taken in different directions.

So far as possible, plans, elevations and sections should be
related so that the drawing can be more easily "read"; elevations
should be above plans, and sections in line horizontally with
elevations.

Fig. 95 shows a drawing of a simple garden shelter in orthographic projection.

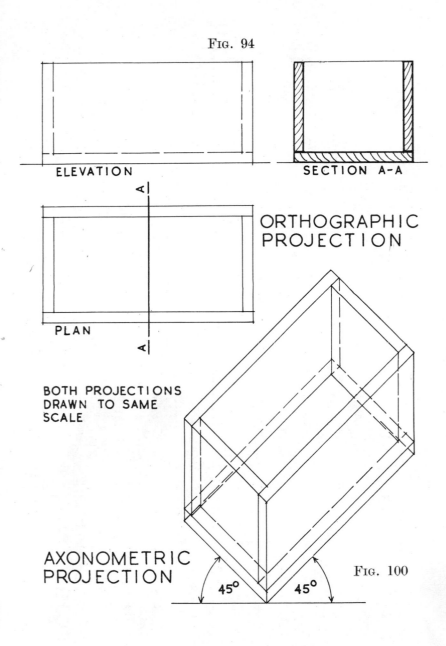

F<small>IG</small>. 94

ELEVATION

SECTION A-A

A

ORTHOGRAPHIC
PROJECTION

PLAN

A

BOTH PROJECTIONS
DRAWN TO SAME
SCALE

AXONOMETRIC
PROJECTION

45° 45°

F<small>IG</small>. 100

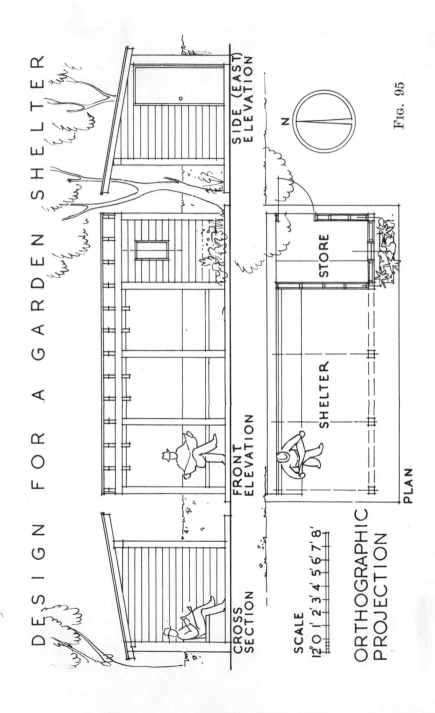

DESIGN FOR A GARDEN SHELTER

SIDE (EAST) ELEVATION

FRONT ELEVATION

CROSS SECTION

STORE

SHELTER

PLAN

N

SCALE
12" 0 1' 2' 3' 4' 5' 6' 7' 8'

ORTHOGRAPHIC PROJECTION

Fig. 95

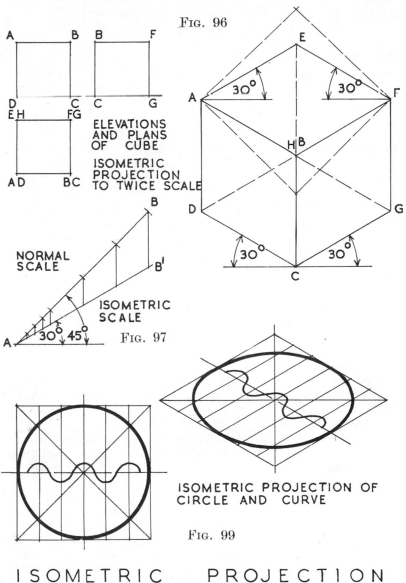

Fig. 96

A   B   B   F

D   C   C   G
E H   FG

**ELEVATIONS
AND PLANS
OF CUBE**

**ISOMETRIC
PROJECTION
TO TWICE SCALE**

A D   B C

E

30°   30°

A   F

H B

D   G

30°   30°

C

B

**NORMAL
SCALE**

B'

**ISOMETRIC
SCALE**

A   30°   45°   Fig. 97

**ISOMETRIC PROJECTION OF
CIRCLE AND CURVE**

Fig. 99

ISOMETRIC   PROJECTION

Pictorial Projections

These are methods of drawing buildings or objects so as to give an impression of actual three-dimensional appearance.

Metric Projections

Metric projections are pictorial projections in the forms of scale drawings on which the length, breadth and height of a building or object can be measured.

Isometric Projection

Fig. 96 shows a cube in plan and elevation and its isometric projection. In the latter, two sides of the cube as well as the plan are seen. The sides are inclined at an angle of 30 degrees to the horizontal, and are therefore easily drawn using the 30-degree set-square.

In normal practice measurements are made to the same scale as used for the plans and elevations, but to be mathematically correct an "isometric" scale, proportional to this scale, should be used. An "isometric" scale is constructed as shown in Fig. 97. A line $A B$ is drawn at an angle of 45 degrees to the horizontal, and on it is constructed the scale of the plans and elevations; a second line $A B^1$ is then drawn at an angle of 30 degrees to the horizontal, and by producing perpendicular lines from $A B$ the "isometric" scale is obtained.

Isometric projection is particularly valuable for illustrating constructional details which cannot be clearly presented in orthographic projection. Fig. 98 shows a typical example of timber ground floor construction and other instances of the use of isometric will be found throughout this book.

When the object to be drawn in isometric projection is irregular in shape or includes curves, it should be placed in a rectangular framework of lines which, when set up, will make it easier to locate the salient points.

Fig. 99 shows how a disc or end of a cylinder is drawn in isometric. The circle is enclosed within a square and a number of ordinates are drawn cutting the circumference as shown. The square is then set up in isometric and the various points on the circumference can be located along the ordinates. The curve passing through these points is an ellipse. The principle can be applied to any curved or irregular line.

DETAIL OF TIMBER GROUND FLOOR CONSTRUCTION

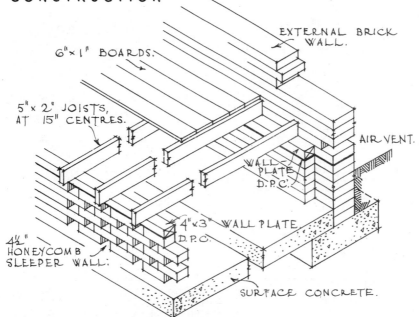

EXTERNAL BRICK WALL.

6"×1" BOARDS.

5"×2" JOISTS, AT 15" CENTRES.

AIR VENT.

WALL PLATE D.P.C.

4"×3" WALL PLATE D.P.C.

4½" HONEYCOMB SLEEPER WALL.

SURFACE CONCRETE.

ISOMETRIC PROJECTION

FIG. 98

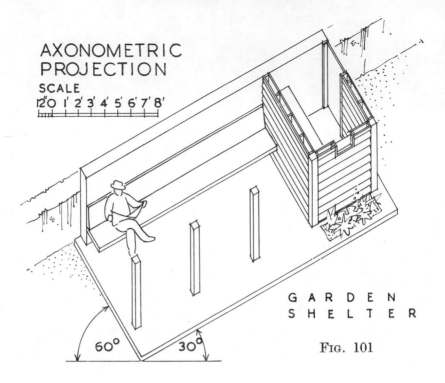

AXONOMETRIC
PROJECTION
SCALE
l2'O l' 2' 3' 4' 5' 6' 7' 8'

G A R D E N
S H E L T E R

Fig. 101

60° 30°

Axonometric Projection

Axonometric projection is similar to isometric projection, but the original true plan can be drawn to any scale, placed with its sides at a convenient angle to the horizontal, and the vertical heights projected up from it to the same scale. Usually, in axonometric drawing the adjoining sides of a rectangular plan form angles of 45 degrees and 45 degrees or 60 degrees and 30 degrees with the horizontal. Fig. 100 (p. 69) shows an example of the former and Fig. 101 of the latter.

Axonometric projection is particularly suitable for showing views of the interiors of rooms, and is much used for interior design drawings.

While usually, in both isometric and axonometric projections, the view is taken looking down on the object, similar views can, of course, be taken looking upwards, as, for example, to show a ceiling treatment.

OBLIQUE
PROJECTION

**BOX SHOWN IN
PREVIOUS ORTHO-
GRAPHIC PROJECTION**

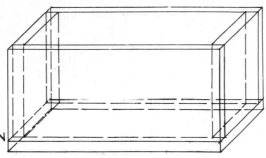

FIG. 102

ELEVATION

SCALE 0″ 3″ 6″ 9″ 12″

DETAIL OF TUSK
TENON JOINT

FIG. 103

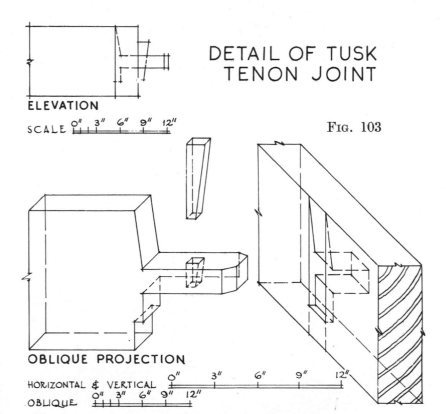

OBLIQUE PROJECTION

HORIZONTAL & VERTICAL 0″ 3″ 6″ 9″ 12″

OBLIQUE 0″ 3″ 6″ 9″ 12″

Oblique Projection

This also is like isometric projection. The principle will be seen by reference to Fig. 102, showing a box drawn in this manner. One side is drawn in true elevation, and lines at right-angles to it on plan are drawn inclined at an angle of 45 degrees to the horizontal. In this projection it is usual to draw the vertical and horizontal lines to the true scale and inclined lines at half the true scale. Oblique projection can be employed for similar purposes as isometric and axonometric projections. It is frequently used for constructional details of jointing such as seen in Fig. 103.

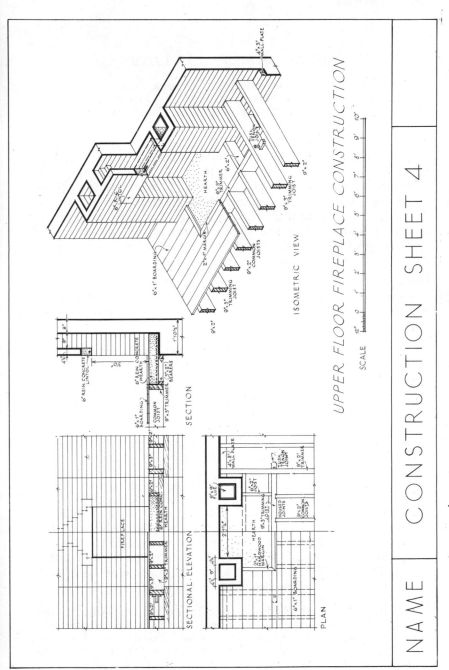

UPPER FLOOR FIREPLACE CONSTRUCTION

ISOMETRIC VIEW

SCALE

SECTION

SECTIONAL ELEVATION

PLAN

NAME | CONSTRUCTION SHEET 4

EXAMPLE OF STUDENT'S DRAWING SHOWING TYPICAL CONSTRUCTIONAL DETAIL ILLUSTRATED BY
MEANS OF ORTHOGRAPHIC AND PICTORIAL PROJECTIONS

CHAPTER X
POINTS, LINES, AND PLANES

FINDING LENGTHS OF INCLINED AND OBLIQUE LINES. DEVELOP-
MENT OF INCLINED AND OBLIQUE PLANES. PENETRATIONS ON
THE OBLIQUE PLANE. CORRECT ANGLES. DIHEDRAL ANGLES

Points

A POINT in space can be accurately located by three axes or
direction lines as shown in Figs. 104. A, B, C are three co-
ordinated planes, i.e. each plane is at right-angles to the others.
Assuming the point to be 3 units of measurement from A, 4 units
from B, and $2\frac{1}{2}$ units from C, it is located by drawing a perpendicular ordinate from plane C (horizontal plane) and horizontal
co-ordinates from planes A and B (vertical planes).

Lines

Lines can be perpendicular, horizontal, inclined or oblique.
Fig. 105 shows how lines in various positions appear in plan and
elevation.

A — perpendicular and clear of the horizontal and vertical planes.
B — perpendicular to vertical plane, clear of horizontal and vertical
    planes.
C — horizontal and clear of the V.P. and H.P.; parallel to H.P.
D — making full contact with V.P. and H.P.
E — inclined to and clear of the V.P.; parallel to and clear of the
    H.P.
F — parallel to and clear of the V.P.; inclined to and clear of the H.P.
G — resting on the H.P. and inclined clear of the V.P.

As an example of the drawing of such a line, assume in case E
that the line is 3 units of measurement long and is inclined at an
angle of 30 degrees to the V.P., and is 2 units clear of the H.P.
The line is first drawn on the H.P. and perpendicular ordinates
are projected up 2 units beyond the XY line to give the position
of the line in elevation. The true length of an inclined line must
always be drawn first in plan or elevation as the case may be.

Fig. 106 shows oblique lines in various positions:

A — inclined to both planes; one end making contact with XY line.
B — inclined to both planes; perpendicular to XY line.
C — inclined to both planes; not making contact with either plane.
D — inclined to both planes; one end in contact with H.P., the other
    end in contact with V.P.

78

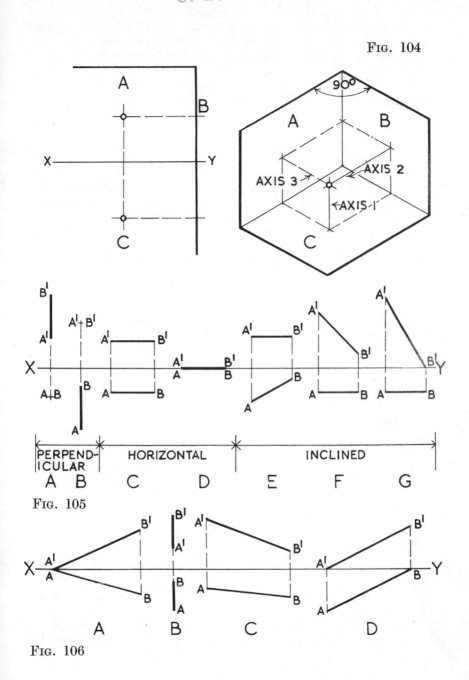

FIG. 104

FIG. 105

FIG. 106

It will be seen that the true lengths of the lines cannot be shown in plan or elevation, and to deal with the various applications of oblique lines in solid and practical geometry the true lengths must be found. There are alternative methods of doing this.

Figs. 107 and 108 show two pictorial views of the H.P. and V.P. In each drawing an oblique line AB is shown on the surface of a half cone. The vertex of the cone in each case represents one end of the line, the other end of which is at the base. Then, by rotating the line about the surface of the cone its true length can be found on the H.P. or V.P.

Fig. 109 in plan and elevation relates to the pictorial view of Fig. 107. The line AB is drawn at an angle of 30 degrees to the V.P. and 45 degrees to the H.P.; one end contacting both planes. The true length of the line is found by drawing an arc from A with centre B to contact the XY li.1e, from which point a perpendicular is drawn to cut a horizontal line from A^1. By drawing from the point of intersection to B the true length of the line is found. Similarly, by drawing an arc from A^1, as shown.

Another method is also shown in Fig. 109: an auxiliary elevation is produced on AB by drawing a line at right-angles from A and by marking on it the vertical distance of A^1 from the XY line, giving point A^2, which joined to B gives the true length.

Fig. 110 relates to the pictorial view of Fig. 108, the oblique line being drawn at an angle of 60 degrees to the V.P. and 60 degrees to the H.P., with one end contacting the V.P. The true length of the line is found by taking B as centre and with BA as radius drawing an arc to contact the XY line at A^2, which joined to B^1 gives the true length. Similarly, by taking A^1 as centre and A^1B^1 as radius, as shown. The true length of the line can also be obtained by means of an auxiliary plan or elevation as previously described.

Fig. 111 is a further illustration of the methods used to find the true length of an oblique line.

Planes

There are four classes of planes: 1. Horizontal, 2. Vertical, 3. Inclined, 4. Oblique.

Fig. 112 shows pictorially examples of 1, 2 and 3, and these are projected according to the same principle described for the projection of lines, and it is unnecessary therefore to repeat the explanation.

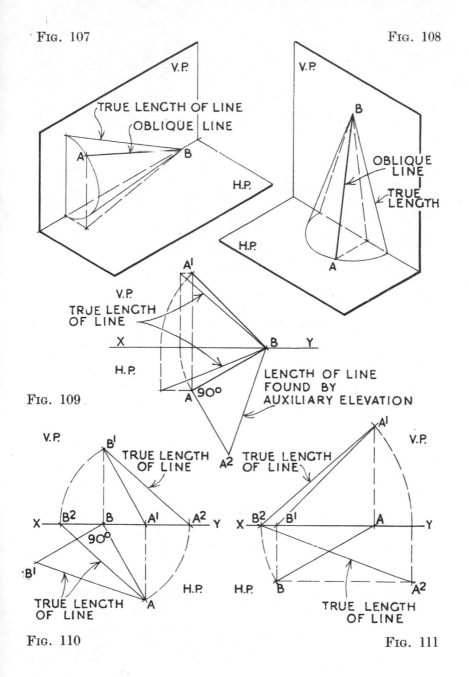

Fig. 107

Fig. 108

V.P.

TRUE LENGTH OF LINE
OBLIQUE LINE

A

B

H.P.

V.P.

B

OBLIQUE
LINE

TRUE
LENGTH

H.P.

A

A¹

V.P.
TRUE LENGTH
OF LINE

X

B

Y

H.P.

A 90°

Fig. 109

LENGTH OF LINE
FOUND BY
AUXILIARY ELEVATION

V.P.

B¹

TRUE LENGTH
OF LINE

A²

TRUE LENGTH
OF LINE

A¹

V.P.

X

B²

B

A¹

A²

Y

X

B²

B¹

A

Y

90°

B¹

B

TRUE LENGTH
OF LINE

A

H.P.

H.P.

B

TRUE LENGTH
OF LINE

A²

Fig. 110

Fig. 111

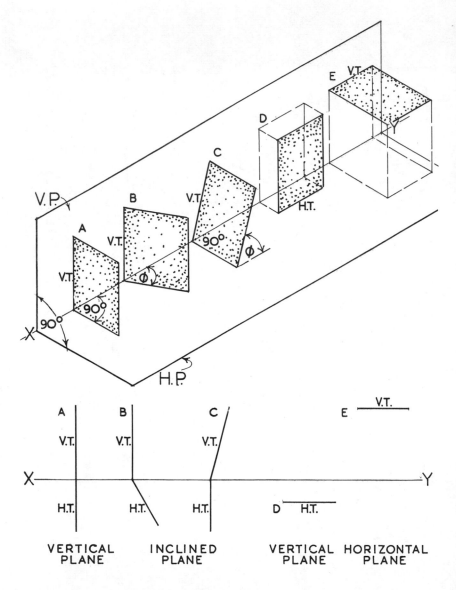

FIG. 112

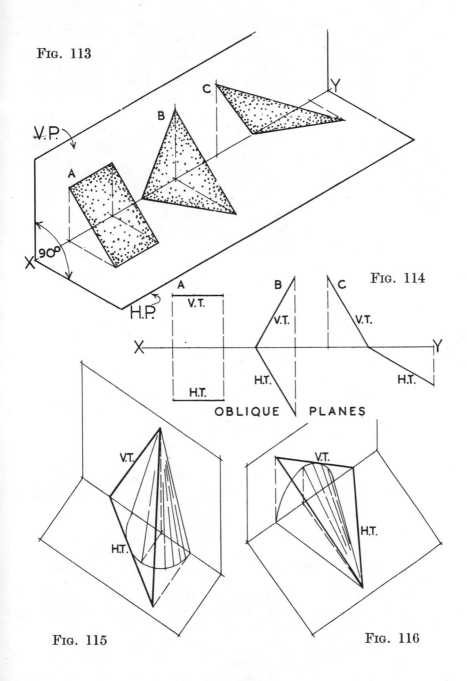

Fig. 113

V.P.

90°

H.P.

A   B   C   Fig. 114

V.T.

X ——————————————————————— Y

H.T.

OBLIQUE PLANES

V.T.

H.T.

Fig. 115

V.T.

H.T.

Fig. 116

Oblique Planes

Fig. 113 shows pictorially examples of oblique planes. It will be noticed that in Figs. 112–116 the letters V.T. and H.T. are used to denote vertical trace and horizontal trace respectively. A trace is a line bounding a plane. Thus such a line on the vertical plane is the vertical trace, and a line on the horizontal plane is the horizontal trace.

In Figs. 115 and 116 pictorial views of co-ordinate planes are shown with half right cones, against which rest secondary planes. It will be seen that in each case the traces are tangent lines to the base and vertex of the cone.

In Fig. 117, the traces, AB and AC^1, of an oblique plane are shown. The H.T. (AB) is at an angle of 30 degrees to the V.P., and the V.T. (AC^1) is at an angle of 60 degrees to the H.P. The true inclination of the plane is found by taking C as centre and with radius tangent to the H.T. describing an arc to contact the XY line at X^1. By joining X^1 to C^1 the true inclination is found.

To find the development of the plane an arc, with centre A and radius AC^1, is described to contact the projection of CX at C^2. C^2AB is the developed surface of the plane.

Fig. 118 shows the traces, AB^1 and AC, of another oblique plane. The H.T. is at an angle of 60 degrees to the V.P. and the V.T. is at an angle of 45 degrees to the H.P. To find the true inclination of the plane and its development the procedure is similar to that described above. With centre C^1 and radius tangent to the V.T. an arc is described to contact the XY line at X^1. By joining X^1 to C the true inclination is found. The development is found by taking centre A and with radius AC describing an arc to contact the projection of C^1X at C^2. C^2AB^1 is the developed surface.

Fig. 119 shows the traces of another oblique plane with the true inclination and the developed surface found as before. It is suggested that the student copies this example on stiff paper or cardboard so that it can be cut out and folded. If the V.P. is bent up at right-angles to the H.P., and the quadrangle A^1B^3BC is folded so that B^3 coincides with B^1, then the developed surface A^1B^3C can be made to correspond with the traces. Similarly, the developed surface AB^2C can be folded up to cover exactly A^1B^3C.

Models can be made of the previous examples in the same way.

Fig. 120 shows two oblique planes making contact. There are, therefore, two vertical traces (AB^1 and B^1C) and two horizontal traces (AD and DC). To find the line at the junction of the planes, its true length and the development of the two surfaces,

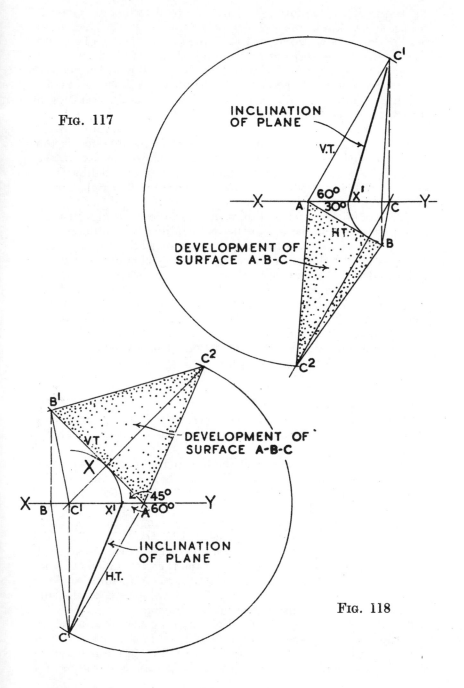

FIG. 117

INCLINATION
OF PLANE

V.T.

C¹

60°
X———X A 30° X' C———Y

H.T.

B

DEVELOPMENT OF
SURFACE A-B-C

C²

C²

B¹

C²

DEVELOPMENT OF
SURFACE A-B-C

V.T.

X

45°
X——— B C¹ X' A 60° ———Y

INCLINATION
OF PLANE

H.T.

C

FIG. 118

the method is as follows: The traces are drawn and indexed. Perpendicular lines are drawn from B^1 and D to the XY line; and lines are drawn from B^1 to D^1, the perpendicular of D, and from D to B, the perpendicular of B^1, thus giving the required line on both the H.P. and the V.P. at the junction of the planes. Then, with centre D^1 and radius D^1B^1 an arc is described to the XY line. From the point of contact, X^1, to D is the true length of the line at the junction of the planes. Finally, a line at right-angles to AD is drawn from B and with centre A and radius AB^1 an arc is described to cut it at B^2. ADB^2 so obtained is the developed surface of one plane, and the developed surface of the other, DCB^3, is found in a similar manner; an arc, radius CB^1, with centre C is described to contact a line from B at right-angles to CD.

Fig. 121 shows a pictorial view of the corner of a hipped roof. It will be seen that the hip of the roof is a line at the junction of two oblique planes, the horizontal traces of which are the wall-plates. Fig. 122 shows the same roof lines in plan and elevation. H.T.^{1} and H.T.^{2} are at right-angles to one another, and V.T. is at an angle of 45 degrees to the H.P. By the application of the foregoing principle, the true length of the hip is found at C^1B^1, and also at C^2B by drawing a line at right-angles to CB from C and contacting it by an arc drawn from C^1 with centre C. This latter operation produces a new elevation. The developed surfaces are found by the method explained for Fig. 117.

The Dihedral Angle

The dihedral angle is the true angle between two intersecting planes, its inclination being perpendicular to the line connecting the planes.

The method of finding the dihedral angle of two contacting planes is shown in Figs. 123 and 124, where the traces of the planes are at angle of 45 degrees and 60 degrees to both the V.P. and H.P. A new elevation of the line joining the planes is first found. Then the line ST is drawn at right-angles to B^3D^1, and a line from S is drawn at right-angles to X^1Y^1 to H.T.^{1} and H.T.^{2} to contact at S^1 and S^2 respectively. With S as centre and ST as radius an arc is described to X^1Y^1 and then continued at right-angles to X^1Y^1 to contact B^1D at T^1. The dihedral angle is found by joining S^1T^1 and T^1S^2. The development of the surfaces of the planes is also shown in the drawing.

Fig. 125 shows another method of obtaining the dihedral angle. The traces of the planes are drawn and the line at the junction of them obtained. The true length of this line, B^1D^1, is found as seen in elevation. With a point T as centre and radius TS

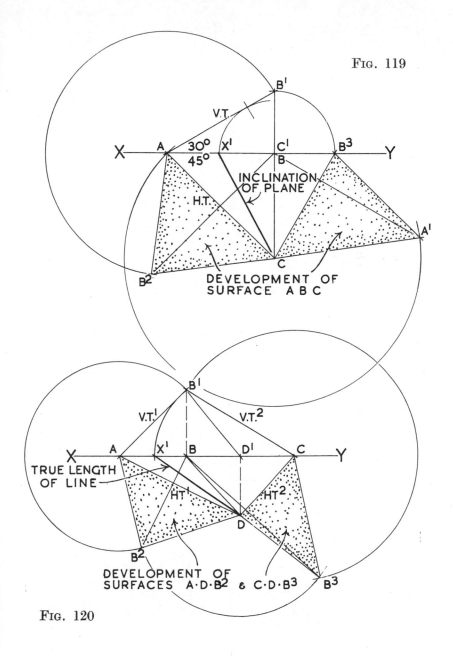

FIG. 119

V.T.

X —— A 30° X¹ C¹ B³ Y
45° B

INCLINATION
OF PLANE

H.T.

B²

DEVELOPMENT OF
SURFACE A B C

A¹

B¹

V.T.¹ V.T.²

X —— A X¹ B D¹ C Y

TRUE LENGTH
OF LINE

HT¹ HT²

D

B²

DEVELOPMENT OF
SURFACES A·D·B² & C·D·B³

B³

FIG. 120

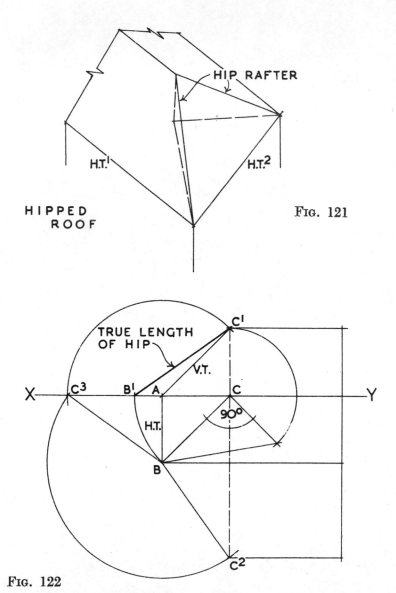

HIP RAFTER

H.T.¹   H.T.²

HIPPED
ROOF

Fig. 121

TRUE LENGTH
OF HIP

V.T.

X   C³   B¹   A   C   Y

C¹

90°

H.T.

B

C²

Fig. 122

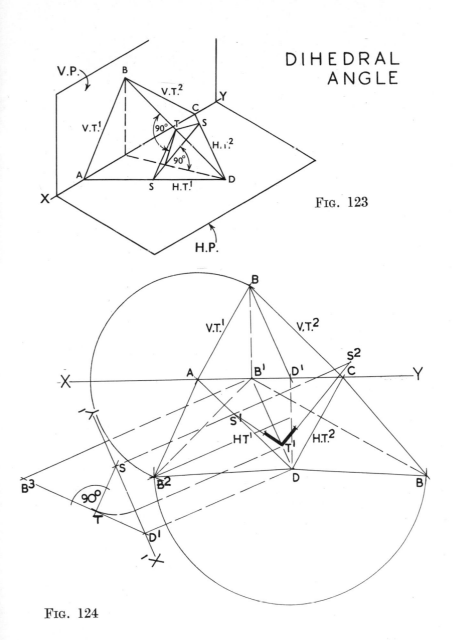

DIHEDRAL
ANGLE

Fig. 123

Fig. 124

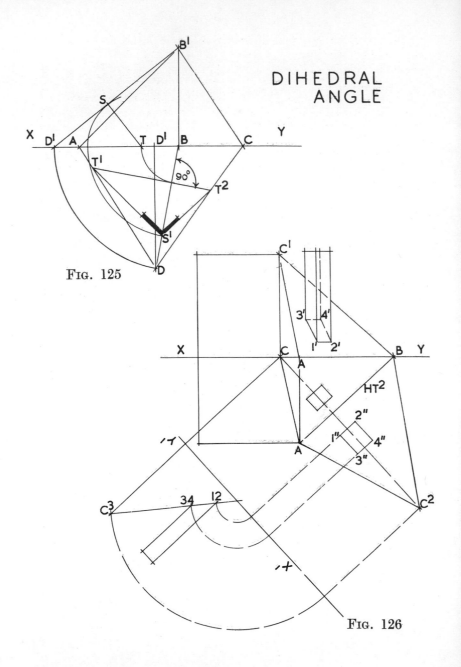

DIHEDRAL
ANGLE

Fig. 125

Fig. 126

tangent to B^1D^1 an arc is described to the X Y line and continued as an arc struck with B as centre to cut BD at S^1. Also with B as centre an arc is described from T to cut BD, at which point a line at right-angles to BD is drawn to contact AD at T^1 and CD at T^2. By joining $T^1S^1T^2$ the dihedral angle is found.

Fig. 126 shows in plan (H.P.) and elevation (V.P.) a rectangular chimney stack penetrating a pitched roof surface (oblique plane). By the application of the methods described the developed surface of the roof is found, and the true shape of the hole caused by the penetration of the stack is found with the help of a new elevation.

Fig. 127 shows in plan and elevation an oblique plane penetrated by a right cone. The development of the surface of the plane and the true shape of the hole are found as in the previous example.

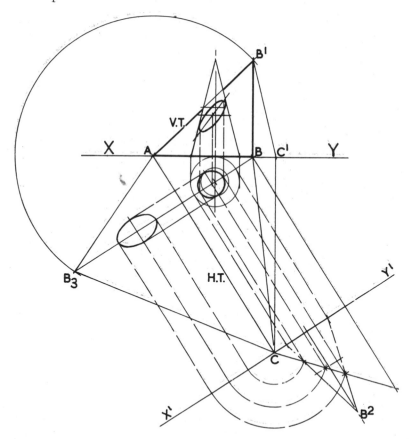

FIG. 127

CHAPTER XI
INCLINED PROJECTION OF SOLID FIGURES

APPLICATION TO GEOMETRIC SOLIDS AND BUILDING FORMS

A SOLID figure may be placed in various positions in relation to the horizontal and vertical planes (H.P. and V.P.). If an object or building rectangular on plan is placed with its front side parallel to the vertical plane, only that side will be seen in elevation (orthographic projection). But if the plan or elevation is moved so that one or other is inclined to the horizontal plane or vertical plane then the projection is an inclined projection.

Inclined Projection

Assuming the object or building to be drawn with the side of the plan inclined at an angle of 30 degrees to the V.P., then the front view would result in two distorted elevations, although the height would be unaffected.

Figs. 128 and 129 show pictorial views of a rectangular block (which may represent the basic form of a brick or a building) placed in inclined positions. In Fig. 128 the block is placed flat on the H.P. and with its side at an angle of 30 degrees to the vertical plane. In Fig. 129 its edge rests on the horizontal plane, its long side parallel to the vertical plane but tilted at an angle of 45 degrees to the horizontal plane. In both cases the block is in an inclined position.

Fig. 130 shows how the block in Fig. 128 is drawn in plan and elevation. The plan, $ABCD$, is first drawn to scale so that AB is inclined at an angle of 30 degrees to the V.P. An auxiliary elevation is then drawn. From the plan perpendicular ordinates A, B, C, D are projected to contact corresponding horizontal co-ordinates projected from the auxiliary elevation. The elevation is thus obtained.

Fig. 131 shows how Fig. 129 is similarly drawn in plan and elevation.

Figs. 132 to 136 shows various examples of solid figures placed in inclined positions projected in plan and elevation to illustrate further the application of the method. In most cases auxiliary plans or elevations or both have to be drawn. (Note: It is important in making such drawings to index all points carefully to avoid misplacing lines.)

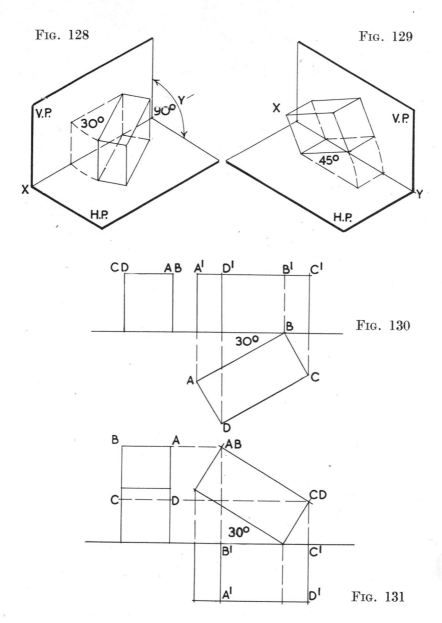

FIG. 128

FIG. 129

FIG. 130

FIG. 131

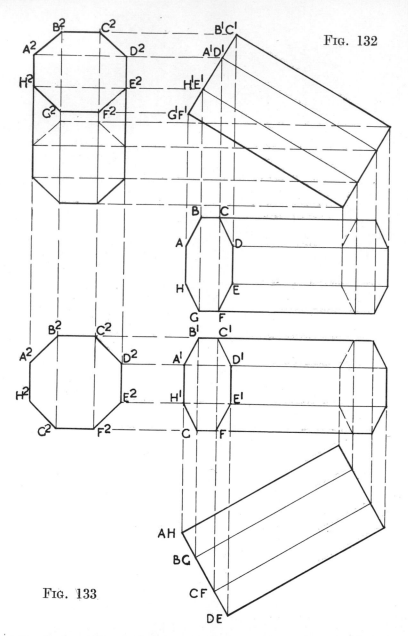

FIG. 132

FIG. 133

Fig. 132—Octagonal prism with one edge resting on H.P., its face inclined at an angle of 30 degrees to the H.P. and its axis parallel to the V.P.

Fig. 133—Octagonal prism with one side resting on the H.P. and its axis inclined at an angle of 30 degrees to the V.P.

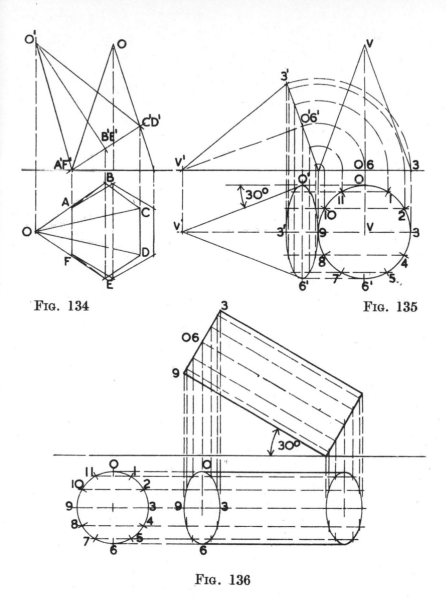

Fig. 134

Fig. 135

Fig. 136

Fig. 134—Hexagonal pyramid with one edge resting on the H.P., its axis parallel to the V.P. and its base inclined at an angle of 30 degrees to the H.P.

Fig. 135—Cone with its side resting on the H.P. and its axis inclined at an angle of 30 degrees to the H.P.

Fig. 136—Cylinder with its edge resting on the H.P., its base inclined at an angle of 60 degrees to the H.P. and its axis parallel to the V.P.

CHAPTER XII
ALTERATION OF GROUND LINE AND SECTIONAL PROJECTIONS

NEW PLANS, ELEVATIONS AND SECTIONS OF GEOMETRICAL SOLIDS
AND BUILDING FORMS

THIS chapter, following on from the previous description of the simple projection of solids, deals with the projections to new horizontal or vertical planes without disturbing the original projections to the co-ordinate planes. The purpose is to obtain views of the object from at least two faces in either elevation or plan.

An *auxiliary elevation* is a projection on any vertical plane which is not parallel to the principal vertical plane, as shown in Fig. 137, where A^2 is the auxiliary elevation of A on the auxiliary V.P.

An *auxiliary plan* is a projection on any plane which is perpendicular to the V.P. and not parallel to the H.P., as shown in Fig. 138, where A^2 is the auxiliary plan of A on the auxiliary H.P.

The lower Figs. 139 and 140 in both cases illustrates how the auxiliary planes can be turned into a common plane for two-dimensional representation.

The following rules should be kept in mind:

1. New Elevations—If two or more elevations are projected from any one plan, the distances of the various elevations from their respective ground lines must be equal.

2. New Plans —If two or more plans are projected from any one elevation, the distances of the various plans from their respective ground lines must be equal.

Fig. 141 is a pictorial view of a rectangular solid standing parallel to the V.P. To obtain a new plan to be viewed in the direction of the arrow, the new, auxiliary H.P. will be inclined at an angle of 45 degrees to the principal H.P.

Fig. 142 shows a pictorial view of a similar solid also standing parallel to the V.P. A new elevation is shown with its ground line at an angle of 60 degrees to the principal V.P.

The lower Figs. 143 and 144 in both cases show how these views will be seen projected on these common planes.

96

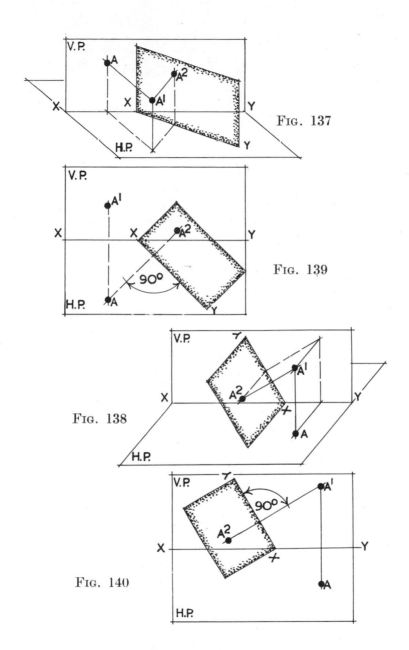

V.P.

A

A²

X   X   A¹   Y

H.P.   Y

FIG. 137

V.P.

A¹

X   X   A²   Y

90°

H.P.   A   Y

FIG. 139

V.P.   Y

A¹

A²   X

X   Y

H.P.   A

FIG. 138

V.P.   Y   A¹

90°

A²

X   X   Y

FIG. 140

A

H.P.

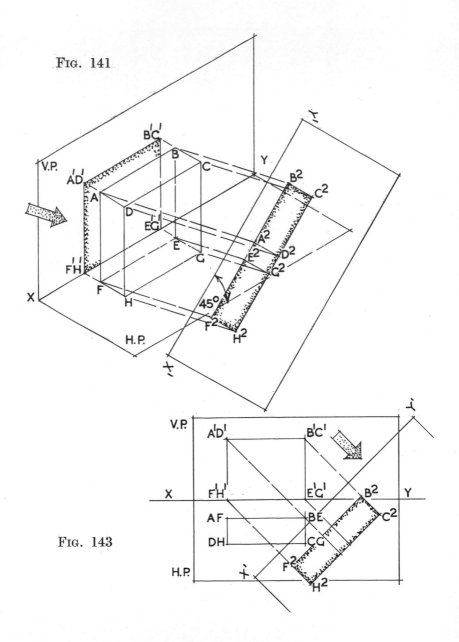

FIG. 141

FIG. 143

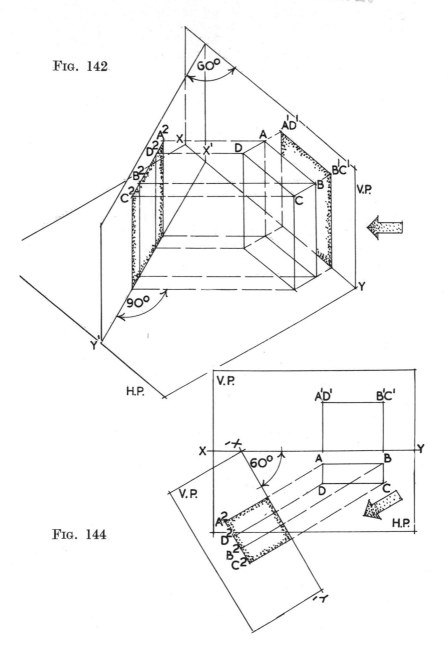

Fig. 142

Fig. 144

Sectional Projections are used to show internal detail. Fig. 145 shows a pictorial view of a rectangular solid with a cut taken perpendicular to the H.P. and at an angle of 45 degrees to the V.P. The projection of the new elevation as shown is an example of a sectional elevation.

Fig. 146 shows a cylinder with its base of the H.P. and its axis perpendicular to the H.P. A new plan also is shown with its ground line at an angle of 60 degrees to the H.P. It will be seen that the method of drawing the new plan is to mark on the principal elevation and plan a number of points (in this case 0–11) at the top and bottom of the cylinder; the distances of these points on plan from the $X Y$ line are plotted from the new ground line on the corresponding projections from the elevation.

Fig. 147 shows an hexagonal pyramid with its base on the H.P. and one side edge parallel to the V.P. A new elevation is also shown with the ground line inclined at an angle of 45 degrees to the V.P. The new ground line is first drawn in relation to the principal plan and elevation, and then the corners, 0–5, and the apex, V, are projected at right-angles to it. The height of the pyramid is plotted from $X^1 Y^1$ along the projection from V, and from the point obtained lines are drawn to the points where projections from 0–5 contact $X^1 Y^1$.

Fig. 148 shows the principal plan and elevation of an octagonal ogee dome, and also a new elevation parallel to the diagonal $A E$, and a section along $A E$ to give the true shapes of the ribs. In drawing the principal elevation, ribs D and E are projected up from the plan by the following method: $C^1 B^1 V^1$ is divided into a number of parts on elevation which are projected down to $C V$ on plan, and continued round parallel to $C D$ and $D E$ to ribs $D V$ and $E V$, from which positions lines are projected back to the elevation to cut corresponding horizontal lines. By drawing a line through the intersections the elevation view of ribs $E V$ and $D V$ is obtained as shown. The new elevation and section are obtained by the methods previously described.

Fig. 149 shows the principal plan and elevation of a simple single-flue chimney stack, and also a new elevation with its ground line parallel to the diagonal of the stack. As before, the principal plan and elevation are drawn first and from the indexed points on plan projections are produced on which are plotted, from $X^1 Y^1$, true heights from $X Y$.

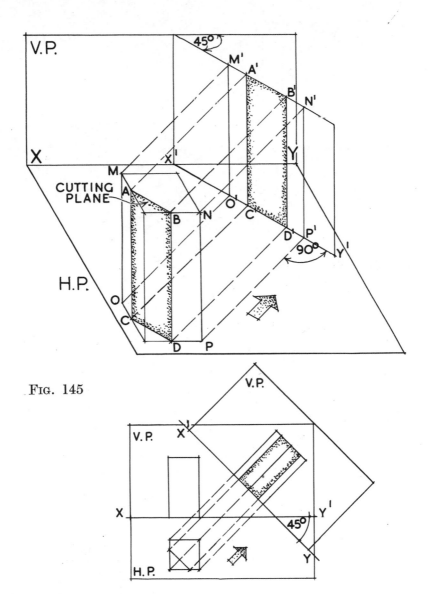

FIG. 145

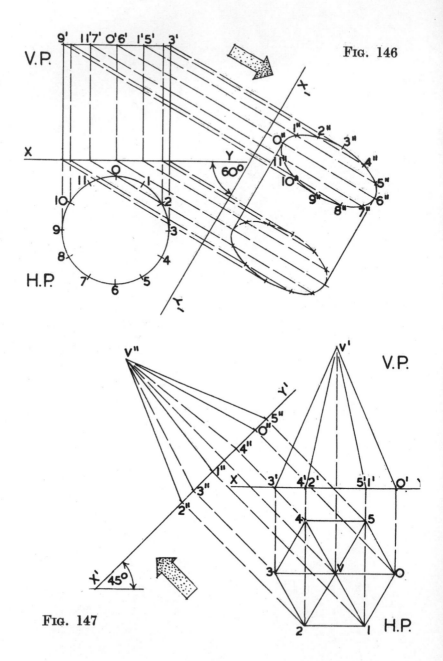

FIG. 146

FIG. 147

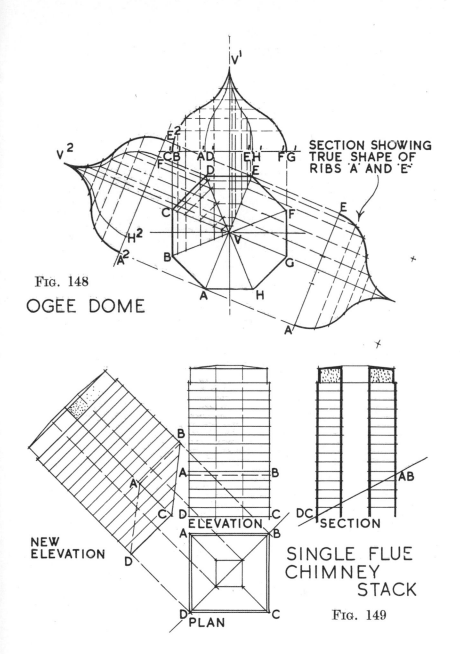

V^1

E^2

V^2

CB | AD — EH | FG
D | E

SECTION SHOWING
TRUE SHAPE OF
RIBS 'A' AND 'E'

F

C F E

H^2

V

A^2 B G

Fig. 148

OGEE DOME

A H

A

NEW
ELEVATION

B

A B

C D C

ELEVATION

A B

D PLAN C

DC SECTION

AB

SINGLE FLUE
CHIMNEY
STACK

Fig. 149

CHAPTER XIII

SECTIONS OF CUTTING PLANES AND DEVELOPMENTS OF SURFACES

FINDING THE TRUE SHAPES OF CUTTING PLANES AND DEVELOPMENTS OF SURFACES

The Prism

FIG. 150 shows an octagonal prism cut by an inclined plane at an angle of 30 degrees to the H.P. The section of the cut and the development of the remaining portion of the prism is found as follows: The prism is drawn in plan and elevation and is indexed. From the V.T. perpendicular projectors are taken on which are plotted the distances on plan of the various points from the $X-Y$ line. By joining the points so obtained the section of the cut is found.

The development is obtained by plotting the perimeter in indexed lengths along the $X-Y$ line extended. Perpendicular ordinates are then set up from A^1 to A^2 to contact corresponding horizontal co-ordinates projected from the V.T.

The Cylinder

Fig. 151 shows a cylinder standing with its base on the H.P. and its axis parallel to the V.P. It is cut by an inclined plane at an angle of 45 degrees to the H.P.

The plan and elevation are drawn, and the circle on plan is divided into eight equal parts, indexed A to H. By projecting ordinates to the V.T. from these points and then proceeding as described for the foregoing, the section of the cut—an ellipse—is obtained.

In finding the development, the circumference of the circle should be plotted along the $X-Y$ line extended. An approximation can be made by plotting the chords, AB, BC, and so on. The procedure is then as previously described.

The Pyramid

Fig. 152 shows an hexagonal pyramid standing with its base on the H.P. cut by an inclined plane at an angle of 30 degrees to the H.P.

The plan and elevation are drawn and the position of the cut determined in elevation and projected down to the plan. The true section of the cut can then be obtained as before.

104

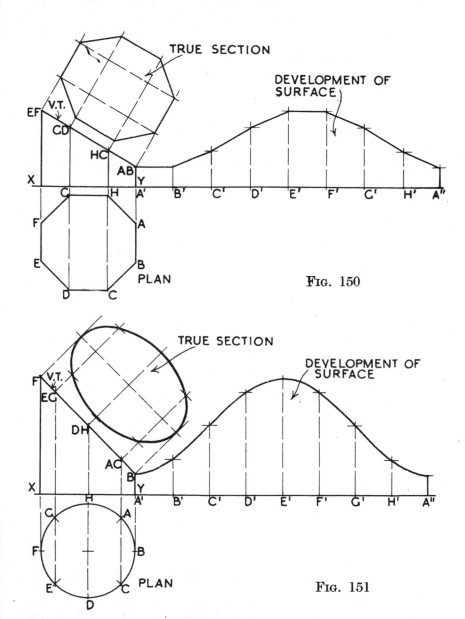

TRUE SECTION

DEVELOPMENT OF SURFACE

EF
V.T.
CD
HC
AB
X
C   H   A'   B'   C'   D'   E'   F'   C'   H'   A''
F'   A
E'   B
PLAN   FIG. 150
D   C

TRUE SECTION

DEVELOPMENT OF SURFACE

F
V.T.
EG
DH
AC
B
X
H   A'   B'   C'   D'   E'   F'   G'   H'   A''
C   A
F   B
E   C
D   PLAN   FIG. 151

The development is found by taking centre P' and radius $P^1 1^1$ and describing an arc, along which is plotted the indexed perimeter at the base of the pyramid. Horizontal ordinates are taken from the cut in elevation to $P^1 1^1$ and continued as arcs with centre P^1 to contact co-ordinates drawn from $1^1, 2^1, 3^1$, etc., to P^1.

Fig. 153 shows an hexagonal pyramid standing with its base on the H.P. and its base edges inclined at an angle of 30 degrees to the V.P. It is cut by a plane perpendicular to the H.P. and inclined at angle of 45 degrees to the V.P.

The plan and elevation are drawn and the position of the cut is determined on plan and projected to the elevation. The shape of the cut is found by the method employed for the previous examples. Note that the true length of $P^1 1^1$ must be found before the developed surfaces can be obtained.

The Hemisphere

Fig. 154 shows a hemisphere cut by a plane perpendicular to the H.P. and inclined at an angle of 45 degrees to the V.P. The plan and elevation of the hemisphere are drawn and the position of the cut is determined on plan. With centre V and radius tangent to the cutting plane in plan an arc is described to the horizontal axis, from which point is projected a perpendicular to the circumference of the hemisphere in elevation, this gives point 2. Another point, 1 (or more depending on the size of the drawing), is taken on the arc of the hemisphere and projected down to the horizontal axis on plan and continued as an arc, centre V, to contact the cutting plane. From the contact points on the cutting plane ordinates are projected back to the elevation to contact corresponding horizontal co-ordinates. The curve—semi-ellipse—of the cut in elevation can then be drawn through the points obtained. The true shape of the cut is found by producing a new elevation of the cut perpendicular to the H.T. as shown.

Fig. 155 shows a hemisphere cut by a plane perpendicular to the V.P. and at an angle of 45 degrees to the H.P. The view of the cut in plan and the true shape of the cut are found by methods similar to the foregoing.

It will be seen that cuts taken through a sphere or hemisphere are circular or semi-circular in outline, and therefore the views of them when seen obliquely in plan or elevation are ellipses or semi-ellipses.

Fig. 156 shows a hemisphere cut by an oblique plane at angle of 45 degrees to the H.P. and 45 degrees to the V.P. The true shape of the cut is known to be a circle. The diagram illustrates the application of the previous methods in finding the views of

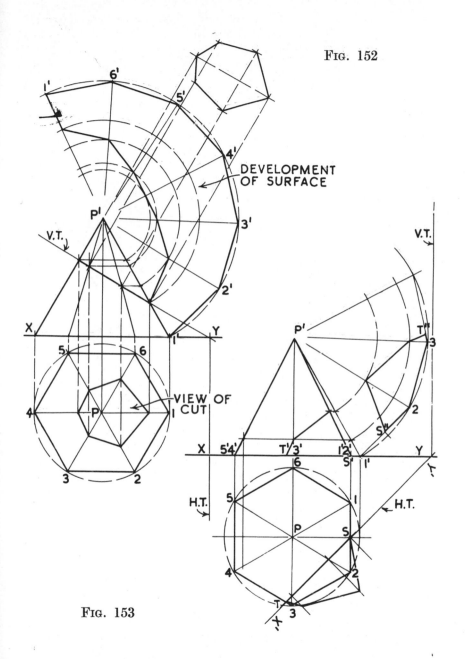

FIG. 152

DEVELOPMENT
OF SURFACE

VIEW OF
CUT

FIG. 153

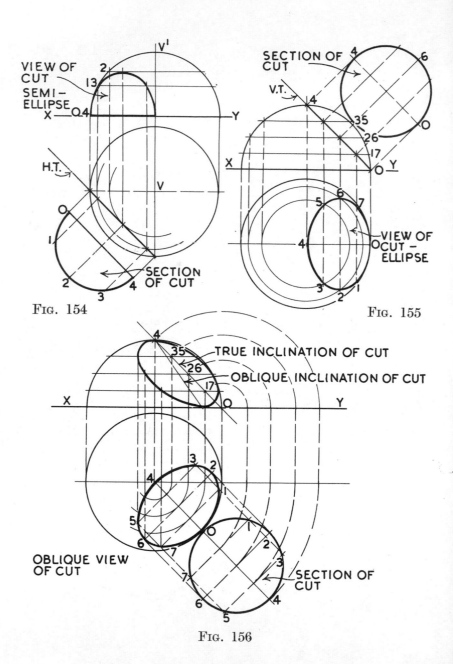

VIEW OF
CUT
SEMI-
ELLIPSE
X
13
2
V¹
Y
O4
H.T.
O
1
V
2
3
4
SECTION
OF CUT

Fig. 154

SECTION OF
CUT
V.T.
4
4
6
35
26
17
O
X
O Y
5
6
7
VIEW OF
CUT –
ELLIPSE
4
3
2
1

Fig. 155

4
35
26
17
TRUE INCLINATION OF CUT
OBLIQUE INCLINATION OF CUT
X
O
Y
3
2
4
1
5
O
6
7
1
2
3
7
6
5
4
OBLIQUE VIEW
OF CUT
SECTION OF
CUT

Fig. 156

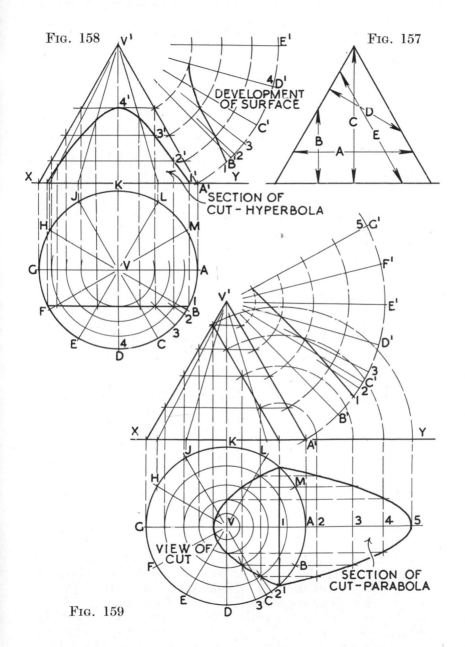

FIG. 158

FIG. 157

E'

V'

4'

3'

2'

1'

DEVELOPMENT
OF SURFACE

D'

C'

4

3

2

B

Y

A'

SECTION OF
CUT - HYPERBOLA

X

K

J

L

H

M

G

V

A

F

B

E

C

D

C

D

B

A

E

5 G'

F'

E'

V'

D'

3 C'

1 2

B'

X

K

J

L

A'

Y

H

M

G

V

1

A 2

3

4

5

VIEW OF
CUT

B

F

SECTION OF
CUT-PARABOLA

E

C

D

3

FIG. 159

the cut in plan and elevation. It is necessary to draw the true inclination of the cut in elevation for convenience of projections to the plan.

The development of the surface of a hemisphere will be dealt with in Chapter XVII.

The Cone

A cone may be cut by planes so as to give sections of different shape. Fig. 157 shows the traces of possible cutting planes:

A — horizontal cutting plane . . . circular section
B — vertical cutting plane . . . hyperbolic section
C — vertical cutting plane through perpendicular axis . . . triangular section
D — inclined cutting plane, not parallel to side of cone . . . elliptical section
E — inclined cutting plane, parallel to side of cone . . . parabolic section

Fig. 158 shows a cone cut by a vertical cutting plane (as case B). Also shown is the trace of the cutting plane on the surface and the development of the surface.

The plan and elevation of the cone are drawn and the position of the cut on plan is determined. The circumference of the base on plan is marked with 12 equi-distant points, A to M, which are joined to the vertex V. A to M are projected to the base line in elevation and joined to the vertex V^1. The points of inter-section on plan of the cutting plane and the lines VF, VE, VC and VB are projected to the elevation. With centre V and radius tangent to the cutting plane on plan an arc is described to the horizontal axis GA, and continued as a perpendicular to the side of the cone in elevation, from which point a horizontal line is drawn to cut the vertical axis at 4. Through the points now plotted on the elevation the curve of outline of the section can be drawn.

Additional arcs with centre V—two in this case—are drawn to intersect the cutting plane on plan. From the points of inter-section lines are drawn radial from V to the circumference to give points 2 and 3, and perpendicular projections are made to the outline of the section in elevation to give points 2^1 and 3^1. From 2^1 and 3^1 horizontal lines are drawn to the side of the cone. With centre V^1 arcs are now described from the intersections along the side of the cone, and from A^1 the distances, AB, BC, CD, etc., are plotted and also the points 1, 2, 3 and 4. By joining A^1, B^1, C^1, D^1, etc., to V^1 the surface of the cone is developed, by drawing ordinates from 1, 2, 3 and 4 to cut corresponding co-ordinate arcs the trace of the cutting plane can be plotted.

Fig. 159 shows a cone cut by a plane parallel to the side of the cone (as case E, Fig. 157). Also shown is the section of the cut—the parabola—and the development of the surface showing the trace of the cutting plane.

The methods of finding the shape of the cut and the development are similar to those employed in the foregoing example and can be followed in the diagram.

Fig. 160 shows a cone cut by a plane inclined to the H.P. but not parallel to the side of the cone (as case D, Fig. 157); also the section of the cut—the ellipse—and the development with the trace of the cutting plane on the surface. The methods are again similar to those previously described.

Contouring

A contour is a horizontal level or cutting plane through the earth's surface, and contour lines to show various heights above and below sea-level are used on many maps and surveys.

Fig. 161 shows the plan of a hill varying in height from 300 feet to 900 feet above sea-level. Contour lines are shown for every 100 feet in height. To obtain a section through the hill, a line X– Y, representing a vertical cutting plane is taken through the plan. Where intersections are made with the contour lines perpendicular ordinates are projected up to contact corresponding co-ordinates, parallel to X– Y, representing to a suitable scale the levels of the contours. The sectional outline of the hill can then be traced. Note that the scale for vertical heights is usually larger than that used for horizontal distances.

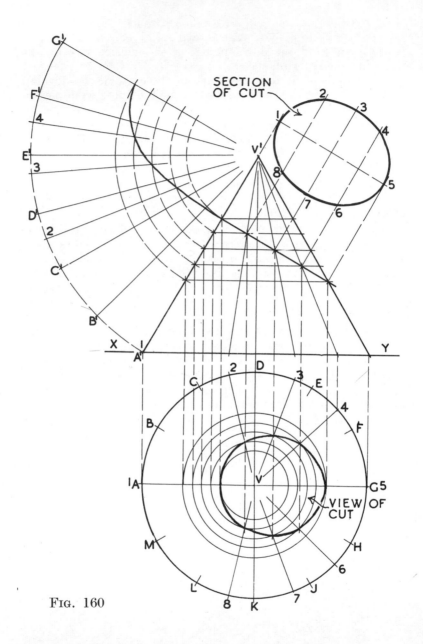

SECTION
OF CUT

VIEW OF
CUT

Fig. 160

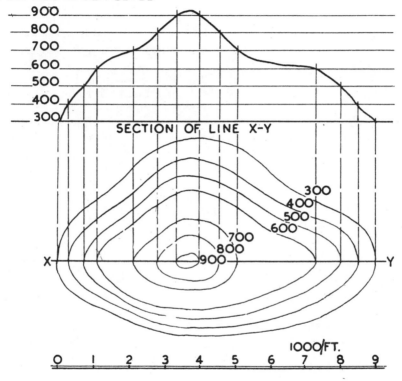

FEET ABOVE SEA LEVEL

SECTION OF LINE X-Y

CONTOURING OF HILL

F<small>IG</small>. 161

CHAPTER XIV
THE HELIX

Setting out of Helix. Application to Practical Problems

The helix is a spiral rim about the surface of a cylinder or cone, i.e. the locus of a point moving round the surface and at the same time advancing axially, the rate of progress being constant in both directions. The advance (axially) per revolution is known as the pitch.

Fig. 162 shows a cylinder with a helical line about the surface. The pitch of the helix and its development or falling line are found as follows: The circumference of the plan of the cylinder is divided into any number of equal parts (12 in this case) which are indexed. The axis of the cylinder is also divided into equal parts (12 in this case). Ordinates are projected from the points on plan to contact corresponding co-ordinates on the elevation, thus giving a series of tracing points for the location of the helix. Units of the divisions of the circumference are then plotted along the ground line of the elevation and perpendicular ordinates are produced to contact horizontal co-ordinates from the vertical divisions on the elevation, thus giving points of intersection through which passes the development of the helix, or falling line, which is a straight inclined line. If the diagram is regarded as representing a spiral (or turret) staircase, each unit space on plan can be made to correspond to a winder, and each unit rise on elevation to the riser of a step.

Fig. 163 shows the outlines of a handrail for such a staircase. A suitable number of winders are set out on plan, which shows the width of the handrail, and the height in elevation is divided into units corresponding to the risers of the required steps (storey rod). Ordinates and co-ordinates are projected as previously described and the elevational view and development are obtained.

Fig. 164 shows a right-handed V-threaded bolt: another application of the same principal. The pitch of the thread is equal to B–B, and if line A–A is at right-angles to the axis of the bolt, then half a turn advances the thread half the pitch.

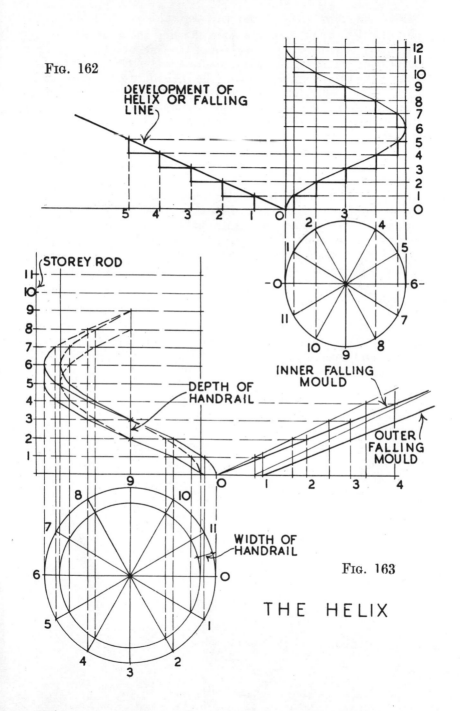

Fig. 162

DEVELOPMENT OF
HELIX OR FALLING
LINE

STOREY ROD

INNER FALLING
MOULD

DEPTH OF
HANDRAIL

OUTER
FALLING
MOULD

WIDTH OF
HANDRAIL

Fig. 163

THE HELIX

Fig. 165 shows a right cone with a spiral about its surface, and also the development of the cone showing the course taken by the helix. The plan and elevation of the cone are drawn and the surface is divided up into a number of equal parts by lines drawn from base to vertex as shown. The height in elevation is also divided into a number of equal divisions. By the application of the previously described principle the spiral is plotted in elevation. and then from the elevation projected to the plan. The curve on plan is an "Archimedean" spiral.

The surface of the cone is developed by taking the vertex as centre and with the length of the side of the cone as radius describing an arc equal in length to the circumference of the base. The base units are plotted on the arc and lines to the vertex are drawn from them. These ordinates are then contacted by coordinates described as arcs, centre at the vertex, drawn from the horizontal divisions of the cone. Thus points are obtained for the location of the development of the spiral.

Fig. 166 shows how the joints of a conoidal arch in stone take the form of a helix. The plan of joint AB is part of the plan of a cylindrical wall. To find the line of the joint in elevation, divide AB into a number of equal parts—3 in this example. From A^1 in elevation a perpendicular line is produced to the horizontal projector of B^1 giving C. A^1C is divided into 3 equal parts, and by drawing ordinates from the divisions to contact corresponding co-ordinates from the plan the helix is obtained.

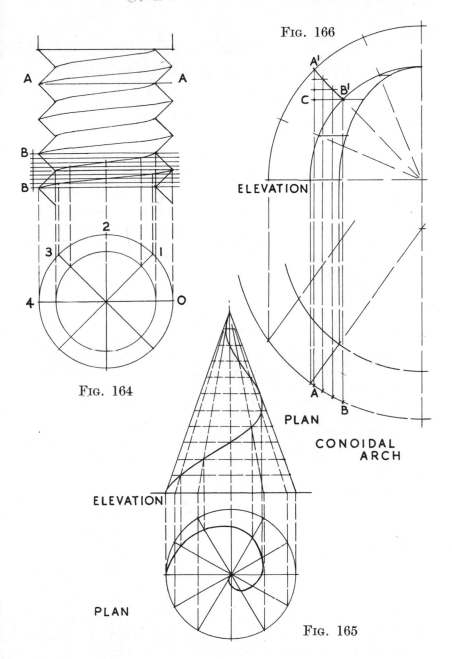

FIG. 166

A'

B'

C

ELEVATION

A

B

A

A

B

B

2

3

1

4

O

FIG. 164

PLAN

CONOIDAL
ARCH

ELEVATION

PLAN

FIG. 165

CHAPTER XV
PERSPECTIVE PROJECTION

TWO-POINT PERSPECTIVE; PARALLEL PERSPECTIVE

THE chief use of a perspective drawing is to illustrate the actual appearance of an object or building, particularly in order to convey an impression of it to another person. An understanding of the principles of setting up perspective is also of value to the designer who requires to make freehand sketch studies for various purposes.

There are a number of methods of making perspectives, all based on the mechanics of human vision. It is not intended here to deal with the theory of the subject, but to explain what is considered to be one of the simplest and most satisfactory methods for all ordinary uses.

Fig. 167 shows a rectangular block drawn in perspective. The following describes the method. The plan of the block is first drawn together with the elevations of the two sides which are to appear in the perspective, all to the same scale. A point, S, representing the position of the "eye" of the spectator, is next established in relation to the plan according to the view required, the precise position being determined by the draughtsman in the light of experience or by trial and error. Lines are then drawn from the extremities of the plan, in this case FE, BC, to the point S, thus forming what is known as the angle of vision, which in general should not be more than 60 degrees nor less than 40 degrees. This angle is bisected and the bisector is the direct line of vision to which a line $VP^1 - VP^2$, representing the picture plane, is drawn at right-angles. (The picture plane can be visualised as a vertical plane on which is projected the image of the block as seen by the eye of the spectator.)

The picture plane can be drawn in front of, through or behind, the plan according to the required size of the picture, which will be larger the farther the picture plane is taken from the spectator. In this example the picture plane is taken a little behind the plan, and to it from S are drawn lines which pass through the salient points, i.e. the corners, AD, BC, FE, GH. Lines are also drawn parallel to the sides of the block from S to contact the picture plane at VP^1 and VP^2 forming, of course, an angle of 90 degrees at S. A line in continuation of one side of the block, AD, FE, is also drawn to contact the picture plane at K.

At a reasonable distance above the drawing already made, a line parallel to the picture plane is drawn. This is the eye

118

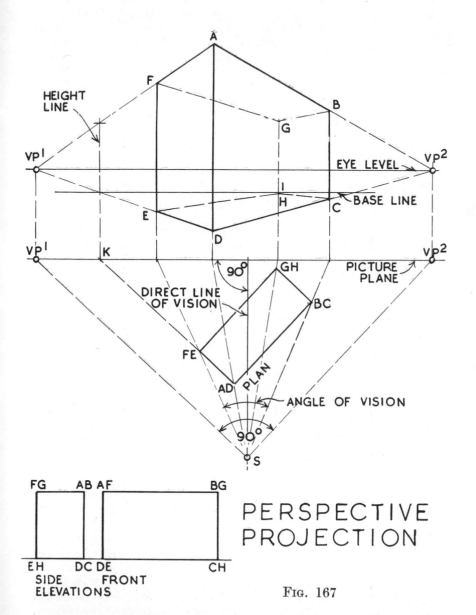

HEIGHT LINE

A

F

B

G

VP¹

EYE LEVEL

VP²

BASE LINE

I

H

E

C

D

VP¹

K

VP²

90°

GH

PICTURE PLANE

DIRECT LINE OF VISION

BC

FE

AD PLAN

ANGLE OF VISION

90°

S

FG   AB AF   BG

PERSPECTIVE
PROJECTION

EH   DC DE   CH
SIDE   FRONT
ELEVATIONS

FIG. 167

level in the picture. It coincides in normal vision with the horizon. At some estimated distance below the eye level, again according to the required picture, another parallel line is drawn. This is the base line or, in the case of a building, the ground line.

Perpendicular lines from the picture plane are now projected up to give the points VP^1 and VP^2 on the eye level—these are the vanishing points to which lines along the sides of the block will converge in the picture. Perpendicular lines from the points on the picture plane are also projected up to give the height line from K and the vertical lines of the block.

The height of the block measured from the elevation is now marked up the height line from the base line, and then by drawing through the points so obtained to the appropriate vanishing points the top and bottom lines of the block are obtained and the figure can be completed.

It will be seen that in this particular example only one height line is necessary, as when one side of the block has been drawn in perspective the other can be drawn from it. It will also be seen that if the picture plane had been made to pass through any corner of the block the vertical line representing that corner would have served as the height line. In simple cases, therefore, it is common to make the picture plane pass through the nearest corner of the plan, but this practice has disadvantages when the object is complex in form.

Fig. 168 and Fig. 169 are further examples to show how oblique lines and curves in elevation and plan can be plotted.

With regard to the result in Fig. 169, it can be noted here that circles on plan tend to become distorted in perspective and better results can usually be obtained by drawing by eye suitable ellipses or part ellipses when the general position of the curve has been plotted. In many other ways, too, the draughtsman will by practice discover means of approximating details in perspective with more satisfactory results than by a rigid adherence to the method of setting up, as no mechanical method is completely free from distortion. And the aim of a perspective drawing is to present as true a picture as possible.

Fig. 170 shows the correction of a common distortion which results when a line of columns are set up in perspective. If the normal procedure is followed as at A, it will be seen that the columns appear wider instead of narrower the farther they are from the spectator. To overcome this effect, which is obviously wrong, lines from the spectator should be drawn through the centres of the columns to the picture plan. New picture planes at right-angles to these lines should be set up to which can be drawn lines from the spectator tangential to the columns on plan.

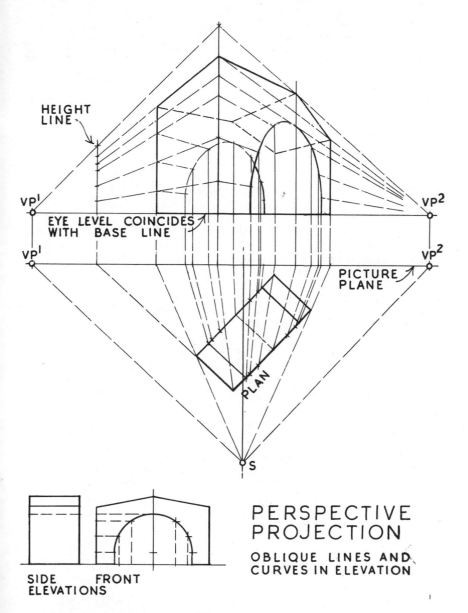

HEIGHT LINE

VP¹

EYE LEVEL COINCIDES
WITH BASE LINE

VP¹

VP²

VP²

PICTURE
PLANE

PLAN

S

SIDE   FRONT
ELEVATIONS

PERSPECTIVE
PROJECTION

OBLIQUE LINES AND
CURVES IN ELEVATION

Fig. 168

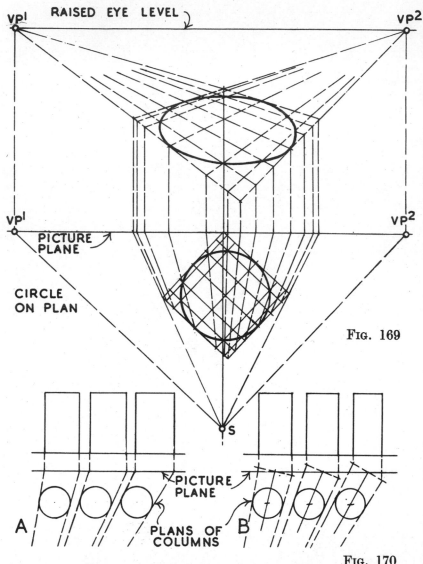

RAISED EYE LEVEL

VP1

VP2

VP1

VP2

PICTURE PLANE

CIRCLE ON PLAN

FIG. 169

S

PICTURE PLANE

A

PLANS OF COLUMNS

B

FIG. 170

PERSPECTIVE PROJECTION

A more correct appearance of the columns can then be obtained in the perspective as shown.

Fig. 171 is a diagram to show the method of perspective projection described above applied to a building. The plan should show all relevant recesses and projections, roof lines, etc., and corresponding elevations to the same scale should be available. The position of the spectator is again determined by the limits of the angle of vision, although the immediate surroundings of the building may be included if desired. A useful guide is to place the spectator from the nearest corner of the building a distance equal to three times the height from ground to eaves. The spectator should not be placed on a line bisecting the nearest angle of the building or the effect in the picture will be unsatisfactory. A good result is usually obtained with a rectangular plan by arranging for the picture plane to be parallel to a diagonal.

A number of height lines may be necessary with buildings of complex form in order to locate features such as chimney stacks, dormers, etc., as well as wall heights and the heads and cills of openings, although the same height line can serve for several purposes. Height lines are always found by drawing parallel to one or other side of the building to the picture plane.

Usually, the eye level is taken about 5' 0" above the ground line—the distance being measured to the same scale as that of the plan. It can, however, coincide with the ground line, or be below it (assuming the building to be on rising ground), or well above it (aerial perspective or "bird's-eye" view), depending upon the effect desired. The general principles remain the same in all cases.

In practice it will be found most convenient as a rule to draw or trace the plan of the building, square with the edge of the drawing-board, fairly centrally on a large sheet of paper and then determine the position of the spectator, picture plane, salient points, etc. When this operation is complete, unpin the paper, folding it under or cutting it a little way above and parallel to the picture plane, and then pin it down again at the lower edge of the board, with the finished paper above, taking care to have the picture plane horizontal. It is then a simple matter to project up vertically as required to make the perspective.

Fig. 172 is an illustration of the garden shelter previously shown in orthographic and axonometric projections (Figs. 95 and 101) drawn in perspective.

PERSPECTIVE DIAGRAM
SHOWING SETTING UP OF MAIN LINES

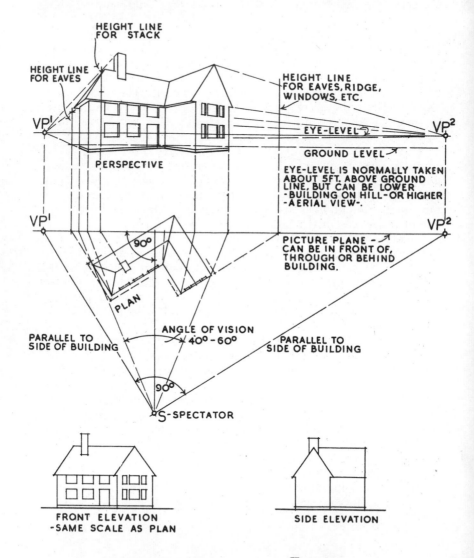

HEIGHT LINE
FOR STACK

HEIGHT LINE
FOR EAVES

HEIGHT LINE
FOR EAVES, RIDGE,
WINDOWS, ETC.

VP¹

VP²

EYE-LEVEL

GROUND LEVEL

PERSPECTIVE

EYE-LEVEL IS NORMALLY TAKEN
ABOUT 5FT. ABOVE GROUND
LINE, BUT CAN BE LOWER
-BUILDING ON HILL-OR HIGHER
-AERIAL VIEW-.

VP¹

VP²

90°

PICTURE PLANE -
CAN BE IN FRONT OF,
THROUGH OR BEHIND
BUILDING.

PLAN

PARALLEL TO
SIDE OF BUILDING

ANGLE OF VISION
40°-60°

PARALLEL TO
SIDE OF BUILDING

90°

S-SPECTATOR

FRONT ELEVATION
-SAME SCALE AS PLAN

SIDE ELEVATION

Fig. 171

A GARDEN SHELTER

FIG. 172. PERSPECTIVE DRAWING OF GARDEN SHELTER SET UP FROM THE ORTHOGRAPHIC
PROJECTION ILLUSTRATED IN FIG. 95. THE SHADOWS WERE CONVENTIONALLY CAST AND
THE DRAWING RENDERED IN WATER COLOUR WASHES

Parallel Perspective

Fig. 173 illustrates the principles of setting up a parallel or "one-point" perspective, which is particularly suitable for interiors and long vistas.

$ABCD$ represents the plan of a square which is subdivided into four equal squares. Diagonal lines are drawn in each square.

The point S is the position of the "eye" of the spectator and the direct line of vision passes through the middle of the square and is parallel to sides DA and CB. The picture plane PP is therefore parallel to AB and CD and is also taken through the middle of the square. From S lines parallel to the diagonals DB, CA, i.e. at 45 degrees to the direct line of vision, are drawn to contact the picture plane at VP^2 and VP^3.

At a reasonable distance above the plan a horizontal line parallel to the picture plane is drawn. This is the eye level in the perspective. To it the direct line of vision is continued to give VP^1, and perpendicular lines are also drawn from VP^2 and VP^3 on plan to give corresponding points on the eye level. Thus vanishing points for lines parallel to the direct line of vision and parallel to the diagonals on plan are found for the perspective.

At some distance below the eye level—a distance in accordance with the required height of the "eye" above the level of the square—a line P^1P^1 is drawn. By projecting to this line various key-points from PP and by drawing through them from the appropriate vanishing points the perspective of the square $A^1B^1C^1D^1$ can be completed as shown.

Any point on plan, E in this example, can be found by drawing from it a parallel to either diagonal (i.e. at 45 degrees) to the picture plane PP. From the point of contact G and from E perpendicular lines are projected up to cut P^1P^1. By drawing from the appropriate vanishing point lines G^1E^1 and F^1E^1 can be found and the position of E in the perspective at E^1 is located.

To find the position of E if above the level of the plan, its true height is measured vertically at G^1 to give G^2 through which a line is drawn from the appropriate vanishing point, VP^3, to intersect a vertical line from E^1, thus locating the required point in the perspective at E^2.

Any points or lines either in front of or behind the picture plane can be found by similar applications.

Fig. 174 shows the above method used to draw the perspective view of a room which has three windows along one side, a recess at the end, and which contains a rectangular box or desk.

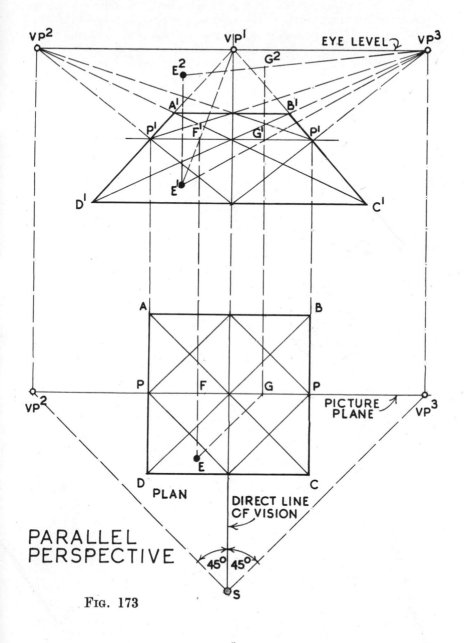

PARALLEL
PERSPECTIVE

Fig. 173

The end wall is taken as the picture plane so that its elevation drawn to the same scale as the plan is a convenient basis for the establishment of the side walls, floor, ceiling, etc. The position of the spectator is determined according to the view required, but the direct line of vision must be parallel to the sides of the room.

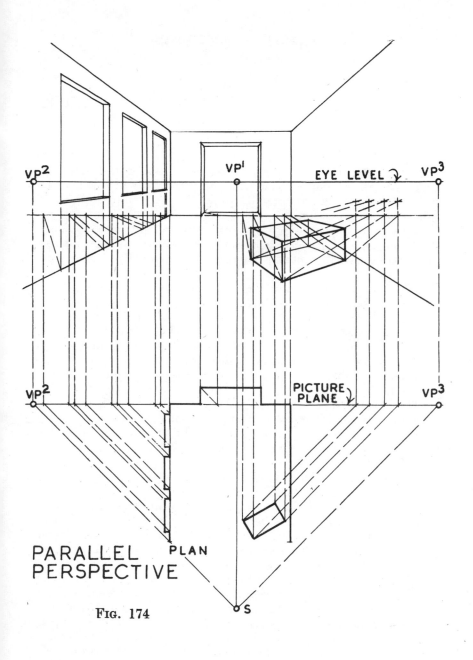

VP²   VP¹   EYE LEVEL   VP³

PICTURE PLANE

VP²   VP³

PLAN

PARALLEL
PERSPECTIVE

S

FIG. 174

PRACTICAL GEOMETRY

CHAPTER XVI
INTERSECTIONS AND DEVELOPMENTS OF SURFACES

Pipes, Vaults, Dormers, etc. Domical and Other Surfaces;
True Shapes of Ribs, etc.

This chapter deals with the methods of obtaining the shapes of various surfaces and of constructional members, which cannot be fully described in orthographic projection, e.g. intersections of pipes, shuttering for reinforced concrete vaults, domes and bridges, areas of curved plaster-work, ribs for domes, etc. Without such geometrical methods it would be extremely difficult in these and like cases to estimate the necessary amounts of labour and materials.

The following representative examples illustrate the principles which can be applied to similar problems.

Fig. 175 shows two intersecting cylindrical pipes. The axes of both pipes are in the same plane. The line of intersection is obtained by marking a number of points about the section of the pipe seen in elevation, projecting ordinates from them to the plan to intersect co-ordinates projected from the superimposed section of the interpenetrating pipe.

The developed surface of the interpenetrating pipe is found by plotting its circumference with indexed points on a line at right-angles to its axis, and from these points producing ordinates parallel to the axis to contact co-ordinates drawn from the joint in plan as shown.

Fig. 176 shows a pipe intersected by a smaller pipe with the axes in the same horizontal plane but inclined to one another at an angle of 45 degrees on plan. The line of intersection is found by the method used for the previous example, as is the developed surface of the smaller pipe. It will be observed that the developed surface of any parallel rectilinear figure unrolls, as it were, at right-angles to the axis of the figure.

Fig. 177 shows a pipe intersected by a smaller pipe with the top surfaces of both pipes level and in the same plane, but the axes on plan are inclined to one another at an angle of 45 degrees. The line of intersection and the developed surface of the smaller pipe are found by the methods used for the previous examples.

Fig. 178 shows the plan and elevation of the outline of a skew arch and the development of its under surface. The arch, which

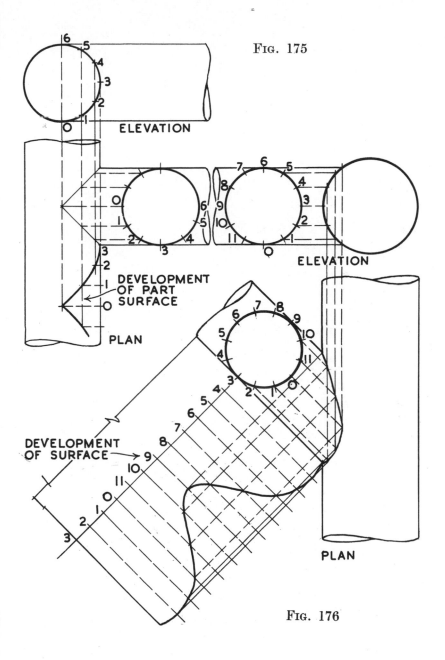

FIG. 175

ELEVATION

ELEVATION

DEVELOPMENT
OF PART
SURFACE

PLAN

DEVELOPMENT
OF SURFACE

PLAN

FIG. 176

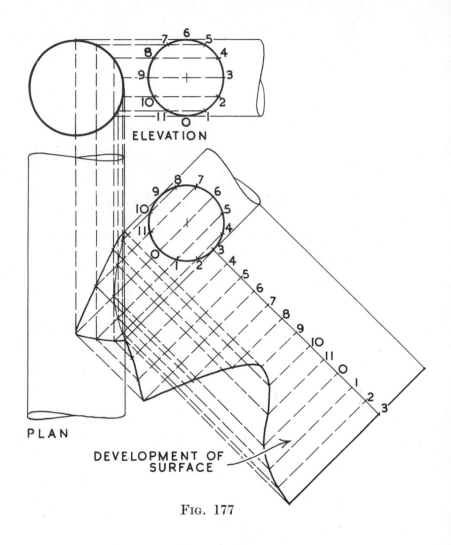

ELEVATION

PLAN

DEVELOPMENT OF
SURFACE

FIG. 177

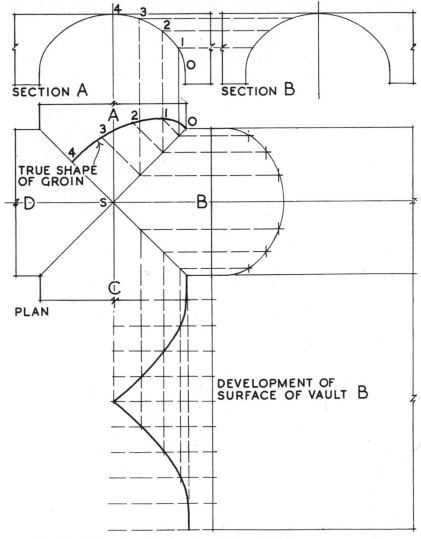

SECTION A SECTION B

A

TRUE SHAPE
OF GROIN

D S B

PLAN

C

DEVELOPMENT OF
SURFACE OF VAULT B

SEMI-ELLIPTICAL VAULTS

Fig. 179

is assumed to carry a road obliquely over a stream, is semi-circular in elevation when viewed along the course of the stream, therefore the elevation seen looking at right-angles to the road is semi-elliptical. The development of the surface is that of part of a cylinder.

Fig. 179 shows the plan and sectional elevation of the outlines of intersecting equal semi-elliptical vaults and also the development, by the method previously dealt with, of the under surfaces, which might be required for estimating concrete and shuttering quantities. The true shape of the groin, which would be the shape of wood centres required to support shutter boards, is shown obtained by projecting a new section from the line of the groin SO on plan.

Fig. 180 shows the plan, section and elevation of a pitched roof intersected by semi-circular headed dormer window, which might be covered with sheet lead. The developed surface of the required lead is found as indicated. A number of points are marked around the front elevation of the dormer and projected to the section and thence to the plan to obtain the line of intersection. The development is then obtained from the plan in the manner of previous examples.

Fig. 181 shows how the surface of a hemispherical dome is developed. Alternative methods are given. (Note: It is impossible accurately to develop the surface of a figure of double curvature; these methods are, however, satisfactory for all practical purposes).

One method is to develop the zones of the hemisphere, which is first drawn in plan and elevation. The elevation is divided into zones by a number of horizontal lines: A, B, C, D, etc., which are projected to the plan where they are represented by circles. The outer circumference on plan is divided into a number of equal units indicated by the points: 0, 1, 2, 3, etc., from which lines are drawn to the centre. In developing zone BC, i.e. the surface lying between lines B and C, a straight line is drawn through B and C on elevation to contact the vertical axis produced at R. With centre R and radii RB and RC arcs are described along which are marked the distances obtained on plan where the lines from points 0, 1, 2, 3, etc., cut the appropriate circles. (Note: Only a portion of the development of zone BC is shown on the drawing.)

Another method is to develop the surface of a sector (the gore or lune). This is done by drawing the plan and elevation of the dome divided into zones and sectors as before, and then plotting the distances from A to F on elevation along a line bisecting one of the sectors, say 0–1, on plan. With radii equal to those of the corresponding circles on plan, arcs are described through the plotted points as shown. Ordinates are produced from the

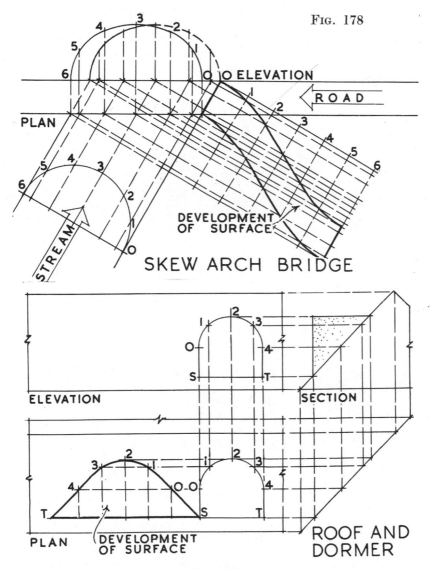

FIG. 178

ELEVATION

ROAD

PLAN

DEVELOPMENT
OF SURFACE

STREAM

SKEW ARCH BRIDGE

ELEVATION

SECTION

PLAN

DEVELOPMENT
OF SURFACE

ROOF AND
DORMER

FIG. 180

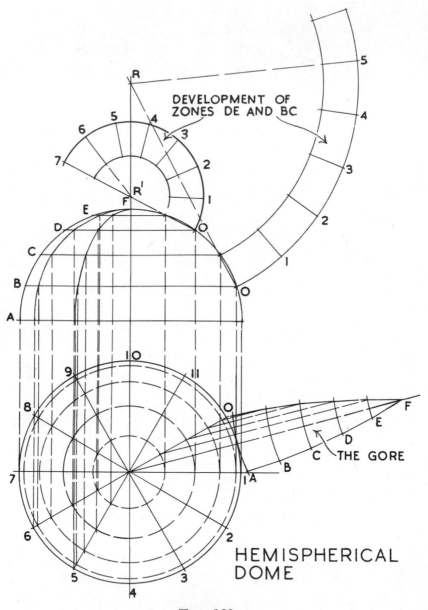

DEVELOPMENT OF
ZONES DE AND BC

THE GORE

HEMISPHERICAL
DOME

FIG. 181

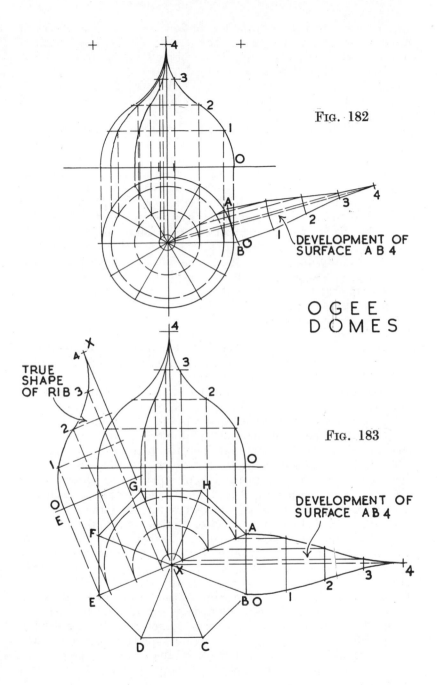

Fig. 182

DEVELOPMENT OF
SURFACE A B 4

O G E E
D O M E S

TRUE
SHAPE
OF RIB 3

Fig. 183

DEVELOPMENT OF
SURFACE A B 4

appropriate arcs of the sector to contact the co-ordinate arcs in the development. By joining the points so obtained with a smooth curve the outline of the developed sector, which is the same as the other sectors, is obtained.

Fig. 182 shows the development of the surface of a sector of a circular ogee dome. The method is similar to the one described for the foregoing example.

Fig. 183 shows the development of one side of an octagonal ogee dome. After the elevation and plan have been drawn, the outline elevation is divided into a number of equal parts, in this case indexed 0–4. These units are plotted along a line bisecting AB on plan. Perpendicular ordinates are projected from the indexed points on elevation to the lines of ribs AX and BX on plan; from the points of contact ordinates are projected parallel to the bisecting line $X4$ to contact co-ordinates drawn through the plotted points at right-angles to the bisecting line. Smooth curves carefully drawn through the points so obtained complete the outline of the development of one side of the dome.

The true shape of the rib EX is obtained by producing a new section perpendicular to EX on plan, using projected ordinates as in the previous operation.

Fig. 184 shows the outline elevation and plan of a pendentive dome and the development of the surface of one of the pendentives. The drawing of the dome is made by describing a circle on plan with radius GA and a corresponding semi-circle on elevation. A square drawn within and touching at the corners the circle on plan gives lines representing four vertical cutting planes. A circle, radius GC, drawn within the square is the plan of the horizontal plane dividing the upper part of the dome from the pendentives. The elevation is then completed from the plan.

To find the development of a pendentive, the arc BD on elevation is divided into a number of equal parts, three in this case, and from the points: 0, 1, 2 and 3 perpendicular ordinates are projected to the plan and carried round to contact $F0^1$ and $C0^1$, from which points of contact ordinates are projected parallel to the bisecting dimension line $G0^1$. The distances 0–3 on elevation are plotted along the bisecting line $G0^1$ from 0^1 and arcs or radii equal to the corresponding circles on plan are constructed as co-ordinates to contact the ordinates previously drawn. By drawing through the points of contact the outline of the development of the surface of the pendentive is completed as shown.

Fig. 185 shows a cylindrical wall penetrated by a spherical apse, with the development of the falling line (line of intersection) about the wall, and the true shape of the rib $0X$. The drawing is made by applying the principles employed in the previous example.

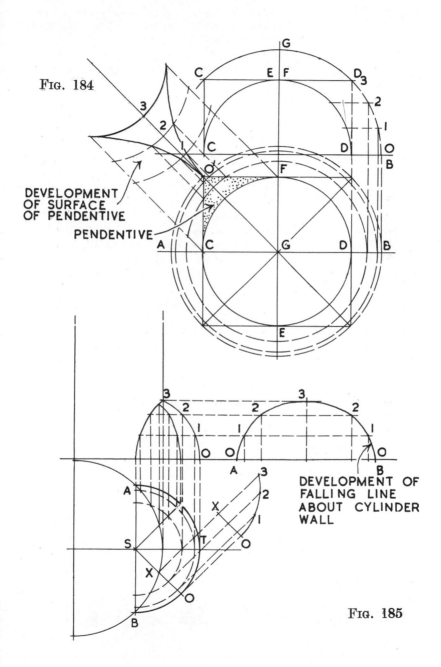

Fig. 184

DEVELOPMENT
OF SURFACE
OF PENDENTIVE

PENDENTIVE

DEVELOPMENT OF
FALLING LINE
ABOUT CYLINDER
WALL

Fig. 185

Fig. 186 shows the plan and elevations of an elliptical dome or lantern, with the true shape of a rib AB. The ellipses on plan and the semi-ellipses which form the outlines of the elevations are set up by any of the methods described in Chapter VI. The lines of the ribs, which are radial on plan, are found on the elevations by the application of the principle employed in the foregoing examples, as is the case with the finding of the true shape of the rib AB.

Fig. 187 shows the outline plan and elevation of a roof which is hipped at one end and covers a semi-circular apse at the other. The developed surfaces of the roof are found as follows: The apsidal end surface of the roof in elevation is divided into a number of equal parts—4 in this case—and horizontal ordinates are projected from the divisions to the hipped end. Vertical ordinates are then projected to the hips in plan and from the hips horizontal ordinates are produced to contact corresponding co-ordinate concentric arcs described in the plan of the apse. Curves drawn through the points so obtained give the intersection of the inclined plane surfaces and the curved surface of the roof on plan. By projecting back to the elevation the line of intersection can be found in that view.

The surface development of the apse roof can be found by zones, as previously described, and the developments of the remaining surfaces by the methods used for inclined plane projections.

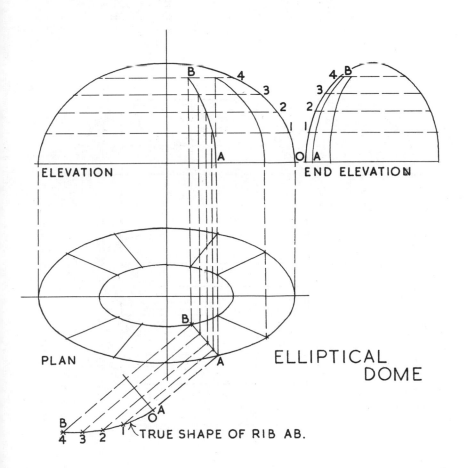

ELEVATION

END ELEVATION

PLAN

ELLIPTICAL
DOME

TRUE SHAPE OF RIB AB.

FIG. 186

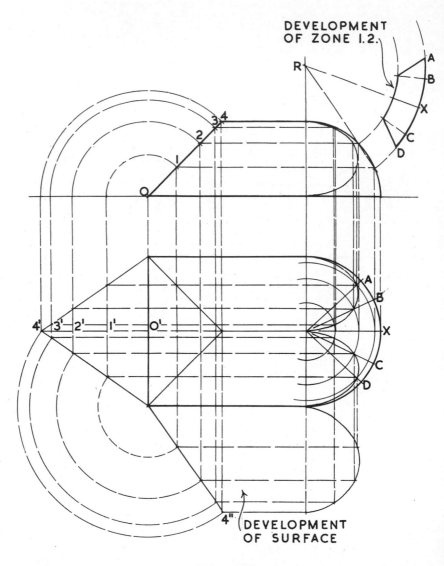

FIG. 187

CHAPTER XVII
MOULDINGS

MOULDINGS, as elements of design, are less used in present-day work than they were in the past, and when used now are of comparatively simple profile. Nevertheless, occasions may arise when a knowledge of classic mouldings is required, particularly with regard to the restoration or extension of existing buildings. Figs. 188 and 189 show typical sections of "Greek" and "Roman" mouldings with the geometrical setting-out indicated. Other examples of common combinations of mouldings are shown in Fig. 190, an architrave, Fig. 191, base of a column, Fig. 192, simple classic cornice, Fig. 193, casement sash style.

However, it is outside the scope of this book to deal with the design and application of mouldings. Students are referred to such books as Normand's *Parallel of the Orders of Architecture* for information in that respect, and the following examples, although based mainly on classic mouldings, are intended to illustrate principles of geometrical construction which can be applied to any type of mouldings.

Intersection of Mouldings

When any two mouldings intersect in the one plane, the junction is known as either (i) a bevelled mitre, or (ii) a mason's mitre, according to the position of the joint. In either case, it is possible to make the two intersecting mouldings of different widths and yet form a perfect mitre so long as the sectional detail corresponds.

Fig. 194 shows a $3\frac{1}{2}'' \times 1\frac{1}{2}''$ architrave moulding intersecting a similar moulding $2\frac{3}{4}'' \times 1\frac{1}{2}''$. Assuming the section of the larger moulding to be known, the section of the smaller moulding is found by projecting ordinates from the salient points of the former to the line of the mitre and thence at right-angles to contact corresponding co-ordinates projected from the side of the required section. The section at the mitre is obtained by projecting ordinates at right-angles to the line of the mitre to contact co-ordinates as before.

Fig. 195 shows the intersection of two bolection mouldings of the same section, one being straight and the other curved. The mitre is not a straight line, and is found by drawing through

143

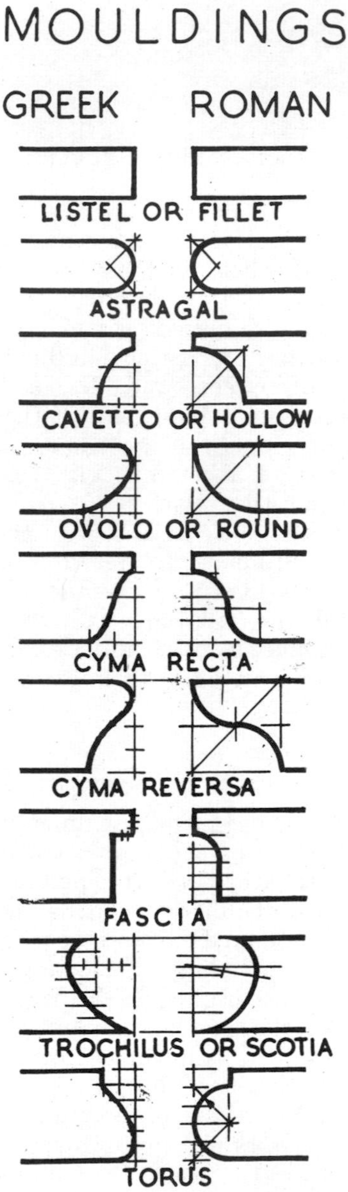
MOULDINGS
GREEK
ROMAN
LISTEL OR FILLET
ASTRAGAL
CAVETTO OR HOLLOW
OVOLO OR ROUND
CYMA RECTA
CYMA REVERSA
FASCIA
TROCHILUS OR SCOTIA
TORUS

FIG. 189

FIG. 190

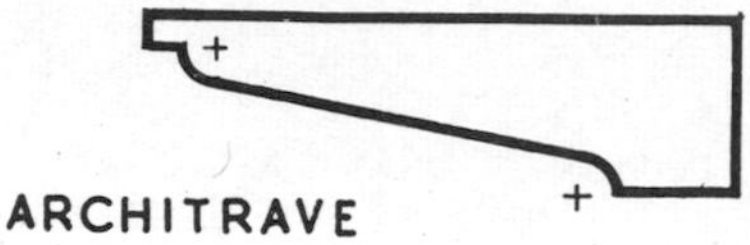
ARCHITRAVE

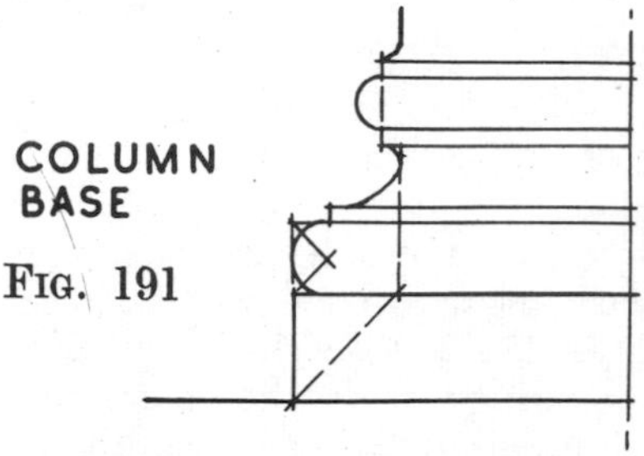
COLUMN
BASE

FIG. 191

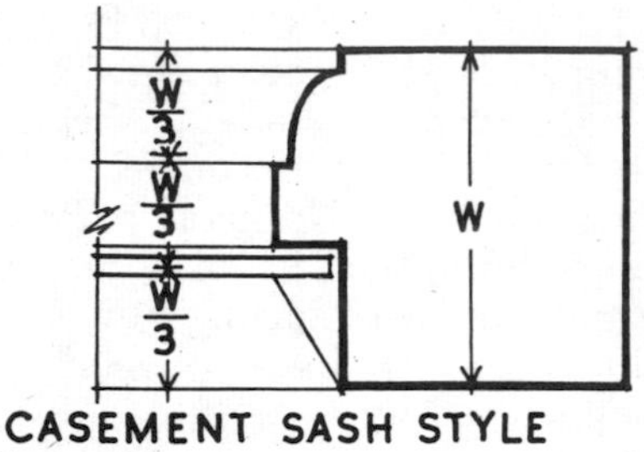
W
3
W
3
W
3
W
CASEMENT SASH STYLE

FIG. 193

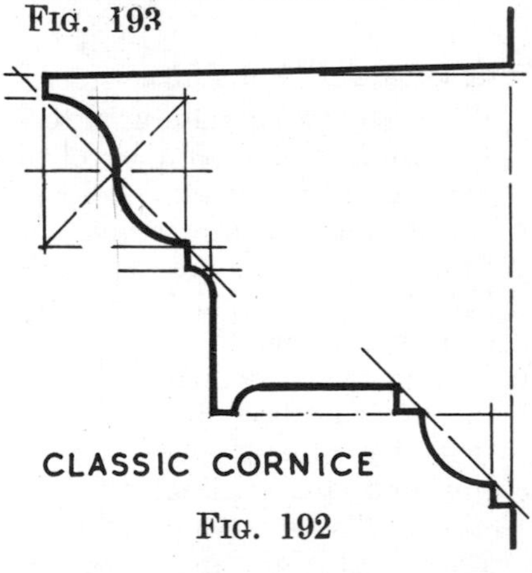
CLASSIC CORNICE

FIG. 192

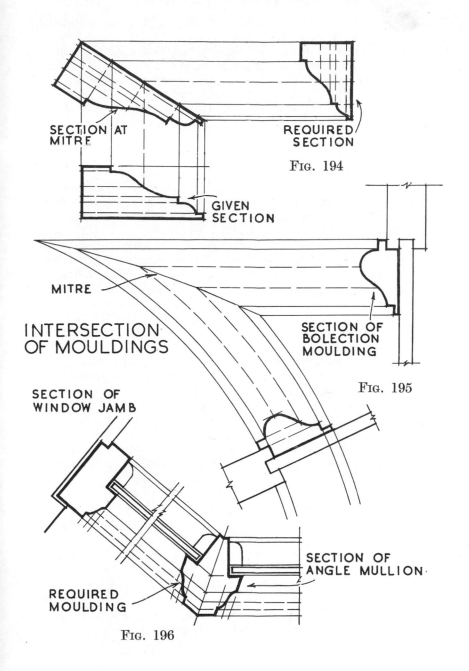

SECTION AT MITRE

REQUIRED SECTION

FIG. 194

GIVEN SECTION

MITRE

INTERSECTION OF MOULDINGS

SECTION OF BOLECTION MOULDING

FIG. 195

SECTION OF WINDOW JAMB

SECTION OF ANGLE MULLION

REQUIRED MOULDING

FIG. 196

the intersections of lines from the salient points of the mouldings in the two directions.

Fig. 196 shows how the section of a moulded angle mullion of a bay window is obtained when the jamb and head of the frame have a given section. By plotting from convenient points about the section of the moulding on the jamb, ordinates can be produced in the direction of the angle mullion to intersect co-ordinates produced parallel to the centre of the angle mullion.

Enlarging or Reducing Mouldings

There are several methods of enlarging or reducing mouldings, or any drawing, such as by the use of the pantograph or proportional compasses, but the following illustrate the application of geometrical drawing.

Fig. 197 shows the full-size section of a moulding diminished to two-thirds its actual size. The full-size section is first drawn, and equilateral triangles are added as shown. The required lengths of the side and top of the moulding are marked within these triangles by the method indicated at AB and CD respectively, and by drawing lines from the salient points to V^1 and V^2 proportional reductions are obtained from which the required section can be plotted.

Fig. 198 shows how a moulded stair bracket, for example, can be reduced in width only for use at the winders of a geometrical staircase. The normal section is first drawn and a line AC, the length of the required section, is drawn at any angle. With centre A and radius AC an arc is described to line BA extended, and the proportional reductions of the moulding are produced in the same way. The required section can then be plotted as shown.

The above methods can be adapted for enlarging mouldings.

Enlarging or Reducing of Surveys, etc.

It is convenient to refer here to the method usually adopted in enlarging or reducing surveys, maps, or any pattern.

Fig. 199 illustrates the principle. Part of a survey is shown enlarged $1\frac{1}{2}$ times. The original survey is divided up into a number of squares and corresponding proportionally larger squares as required are then drawn on which can be plotted the enlarged survey. The use of the proportional compasses is most convenient in this case as great accuracy would be needed.

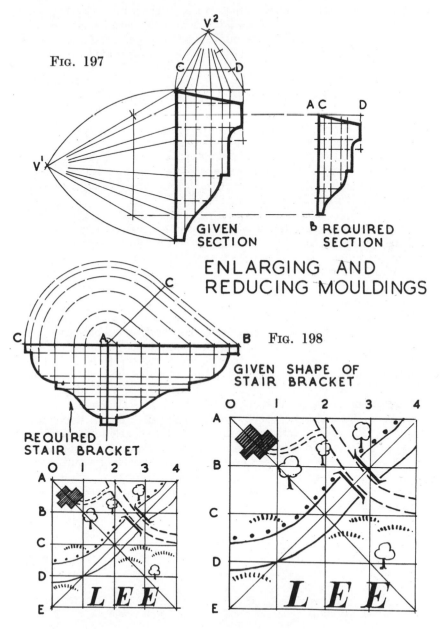

FIG. 197

V²

C   D

A C   D

GIVEN
SECTION

b REQUIRED
SECTION

ENLARGING AND
REDUCING MOULDINGS

C

C   A   B   FIG. 198

GIVEN SHAPE OF
STAIR BRACKET

REQUIRED
STAIR BRACKET

LEE

LEE

FIG. 199

Raking Mouldings

When a series of mouldings (cornice, string, rail, etc.) are seen inclined to the H.P. the moulded section is termed an inclined raking moulding. When the mouldings are seen inclined to both the H.P. and the V.P. the moulded section is termed an oblique raking moulding.

Fig. 200 shows the section of a simple pedimented cornice as used over door and window openings in classic architecture. It will be seen, by carefully following the construction lines, how the section of the raking cornice and also the return section of the cornice in the case of a broken pediment are obtained.

Fig. 201 shows a curved or sprung pedimented cornice moulding. The section of the raking cornice is obtained in a similar manner to the foregoing. Note that the section is drawn parallel to the radiating line of the curve (the normal).

Fig. 202 shows a moulded dado or string in three lengths mitred on the face of a wall, which is in three corresponding vertical planes forming angles of 90 degrees and 120 degrees on plan. The moulding can be assumed to be parallel to the pitch of a staircase, in which case the section of the top landing moulding being known, the sections of the raking moulding and the lower landing moulding, and the bevels for the mitres can be obtained as follows: The outline plan and elevation showing the course the dado rail is to follow are drawn. The section of the dado rail being known, it is drawn on the elevation and plan, and ordinate lines are determined, both in plan and elevation, to establish the mitres AB and CD. Projections from these lines at CD give the view of the mitre at C^1D^1. Ordinates are projected from the edge of the mitre for the raking moulding in elevation. The true shape of the raking is obtained by following the principle used in Fig. 200. The section of the lower return moulding is found by projecting ordinates from AB to contact the inclined co-ordinates. The bevels, required for use in cutting the mouldings, are obtained from the top surface developments as shown in the diagram. The pitch bevels of the raking moulding are found in the elevation.

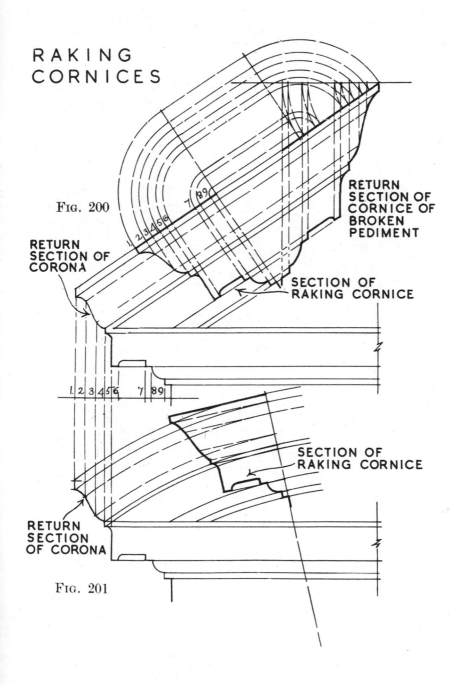

RAKING
CORNICES

Fig. 200

RETURN
SECTION OF
CORONA

RETURN
SECTION OF
CORNICE OF
BROKEN
PEDIMENT

SECTION OF
RAKING CORNICE

SECTION OF
RAKING CORNICE

RETURN
SECTION
OF CORONA

Fig. 201

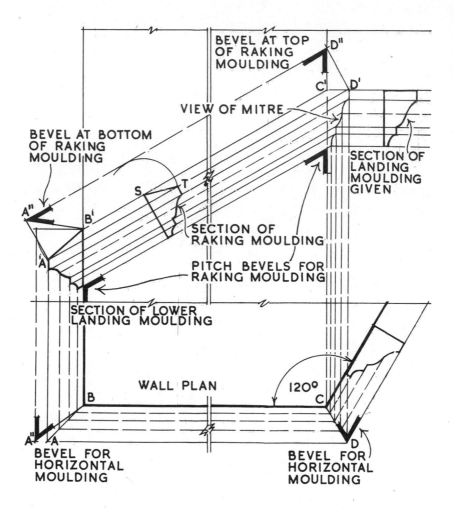

BEVEL AT TOP
OF RAKING
MOULDING

D"

C'   D'

VIEW OF MITRE

SECTION OF
LANDING
MOULDING
GIVEN

BEVEL AT BOTTOM
OF RAKING
MOULDING

A"   Y

B'

S   T

A'

SECTION OF
RAKING MOULDING

PITCH BEVELS FOR
RAKING MOULDING

SECTION OF LOWER
LANDING MOULDING

WALL PLAN

120°

B

C

A"   A

D

BEVEL FOR
HORIZONTAL
MOULDING

BEVEL FOR
HORIZONTAL
MOULDING

RAKING   MOULDINGS

Fɪɢ. 202

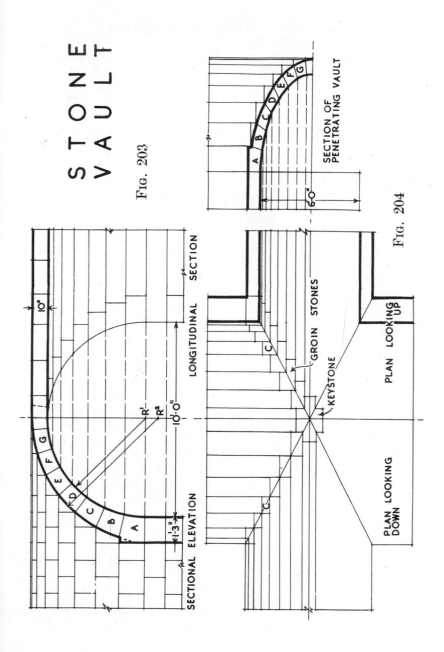

STONE
VAULT

Fig. 203

10"

R¹
R²

10'-0"

1'-3"

SECTIONAL ELEVATION

LONGITUDINAL SECTION

SECTION OF
PENETRATING VAULT

6'-0"

Fig. 204

GROIN STONES

KEYSTONE

PLAN LOOKING
UP

PLAN LOOKING
DOWN

GEOMETRY APPLIED TO MASONRY

ALTHOUGH reinforced concrete has taken the place of masonry to a great extent in many large structural works, a knowledge of the application of geometry to masonry construction is still necessary. The following pages deal with various examples. To avoid the taking up of space in this book to explain technical terms, the student is recommended to refer to books dealing with masonry in detail.

CHAPTER XVIII

STONE VAULT

FIGS. 203 to 210 illustrate the construction of a stilted semicircular barrel vault penetrated by an elliptical barrel vault, the top of each vault is in the same horizontal plane, and the groin lines on plan are straight lines.

Fig. 203 shows a half sectional elevation of the larger vault and a half longitudinal section of the smaller vault. R^1 and R^2 are the centres for the intrados (the soffit) and the extrados respectively of the larger vault. The joints of the stones on section radiate from R^1.

Lines representing the courses of masonry are found on plan, Fig. 204, by projecting down from the elevation to the groin lines.

To find the section of the penetrating vault ordinates are projected from the groins (lines of courses) on plan and the required heights are plotted along them from the sectional elevations.

Each groin stone has two vertical faces. Figs. 205 and 206 show these face moulds for groin stone "C" and Fig. 207 the plan of the same stone, giving the required width, depth and thickness. Fig. 208 shows an isometric view of the groin stone showing how the face moulds are arranged on the squared stone. In practice zinc templets corresponding to the face moulds are used and the waste stone is cut away.

Fig. 209 shows the size of stone required for the keystone, together with the necessary face moulds, which can also be applied to the ridge stones, as seen in the isometric drawing, Fig. 210, of the keystone with adjoining groin stone and ridge stone.

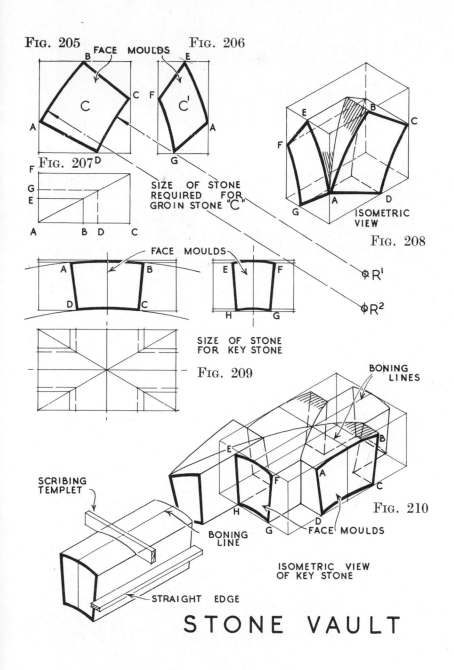

FIG. 205 FACE MOULDS FIG. 206

C

C'

FIG. 207

SIZE OF STONE
REQUIRED FOR
GROIN STONE "C"

ISOMETRIC
VIEW

FIG. 208

FACE MOULDS

ϕR^1

ϕR^2

SIZE OF STONE
FOR KEY STONE

FIG. 209

BONING
LINES

SCRIBING
TEMPLET

FIG. 210

BONING
LINE

FACE MOULDS

ISOMETRIC VIEW
OF KEY STONE

STRAIGHT EDGE

STONE VAULT

CHAPTER XIX
STONE NICHE

Figs. 211, 212 and 213 show the plan, elevation and section of a stone niche formed by niche stones, $D-K$, which can be in whole or part units arranged around the conical boss stone, seen in Fig. 214.

The stones are drawn first in elevation, and must include a keystone, with radial joints from centre P. The joint lines when projected down to the plan appear as parts of ellipses. In dividing up the stones to prevent too much cutting to waste, sharp ends should be avoided or fractures may result.

Fig. 215 is an isometric view of a springer stone showing the application of the various moulds and bevels to the squared block.

Fig. 214 shows an isometric view of the boss stone, the dimensions of which are seen in Figs. 211, 212 and 213, with the application of the front and back face moulds the bevels become automatic, and the conical surface can be worked. The lower bed mould is applied to enable the part spherical surface to be worked.

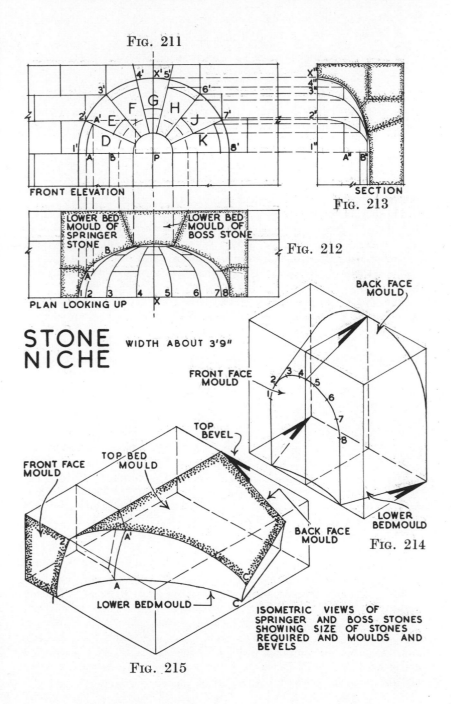

Fig. 211

4' X' 5'
3'
F G H
2' A' E
D J
1' K
A B P
8'
6'
7'
2'
1'

FRONT ELEVATION

X"
4"
3"
2"
1"
A" B"

SECTION

Fig. 213

Fig. 212

LOWER BED
MOULD OF
SPRINGER
STONE
B

LOWER BED
MOULD OF
BOSS STONE

A'
A
1 2 3 4 5 6 7 8
X

PLAN LOOKING UP

STONE
NICHE

WIDTH ABOUT 3'9"

BACK FACE
MOULD

FRONT FACE
MOULD
1 2 3 4 5 6 7 8

TOP
BEVEL

TOP BED
MOULD

FRONT FACE
MOULD

A'
A
C
C

LOWER BEDMOULD

BACK FACE
MOULD

LOWER
BEDMOULD

Fig. 214

ISOMETRIC VIEWS OF
SPRINGER AND BOSS STONES
SHOWING SIZE OF STONES
REQUIRED AND MOULDS AND
BEVELS

Fig. 215

CHAPTER XX

STONE DOME

Figs. 216 and 217 show the half plan, half elevation, and half sectional elevation of a hemispherical dome constructed in stone. The dome rests on a stone drum which has both an external and an internal cornice. The latter has a condensation groove, which could be used for indirect lighting purposes. The stones forming the dome are in horizontal courses laid to bond and with joints radiating to R^1, the centre for the intrados of the dome.

The section of the dome is drawn by means of arcs from centres R^1 and R^2 arranged to give the required diminishing thickness of the shell. The intrados curve is divided into a number of parts corresponding to the number of stones required, including, of course, the keystone, and the horizontal course lines can then be drawn.

The course lines are projected down to the plan—from the intrados and extrados to the axis ST—where they appear as concentric arcs. The lengths of the stones are determined on plan and the vertical joint lines are drawn radiating from R^1. They are projected up to the elevation where they appear as parts of ellipses.

In the drawing two stones in course "C" have been removed to show the view of joints.

Figs. 218 and 219 show the section, plan and the development of face and bed moulds for dome stones of course "C." The size of the stone required can be seen from the plan and elevation. The indexed points 1–4 and 5–8 show the bed moulds of the stone.

Fig. 220 is an isometric view showing the block of stone with the templets and bevels indicated. In cutting the stone the top and bottom faces would be cut away with the application of the top and bottom bevels; by applying the top and bottom bed moulds the side bevels are automatically given, and by cutting the side pieces of stone away, the face moulds can be arranged. The circular-circular cutting can then be carried out with care by testing the surface with straight-edge and scribing templet.

Figs. 221 and 222 show the section and plan with size of stone required for the keystone. The surfaces A, B, C, D and E, F, G, H give the top and bottom face moulds. Fig. 223 shows the isometric view of this stone. With the application of the top and bottom face moulds on the stone the side bevel becomes automatic and with the aid of the scribing templets the curved surfaces can be worked.

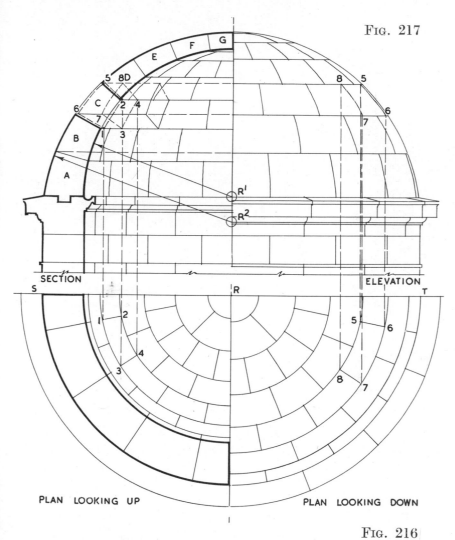

FIG. 217

FIG. 216

S T O N E   D O M E

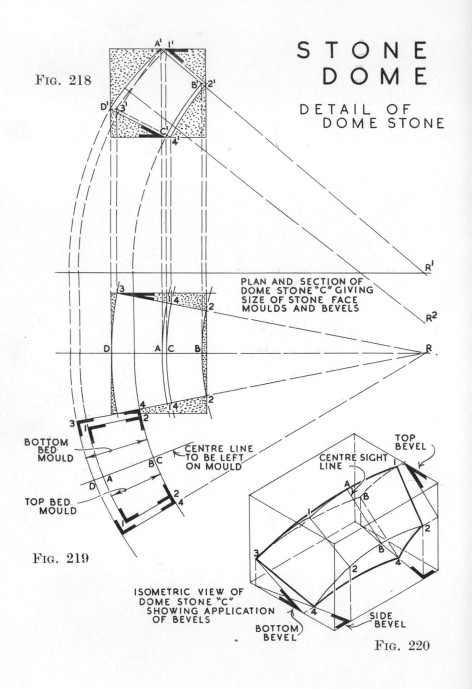

FIG. 218

STONE
DOME

DETAIL OF DOME STONE

PLAN AND SECTION OF
DOME STONE "C" GIVING
SIZE OF STONE FACE
MOULDS AND BEVELS

R¹

R²

R

BOTTOM
BED
MOULD

CENTRE LINE
TO BE LEFT
ON MOULD

TOP
BEVEL

CENTRE SIGHT
LINE

TOP BED
MOULD

FIG. 219

ISOMETRIC VIEW OF
DOME STONE "C"
SHOWING APPLICATION
OF BEVELS

BOTTOM
BEVEL

SIDE
BEVEL

FIG. 220

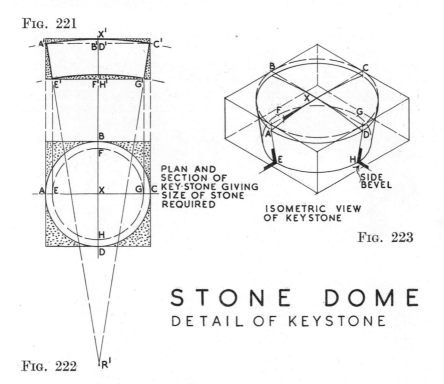

FIG. 221

FIG. 222   R'

PLAN AND
SECTION OF
KEY-STONE GIVING
SIZE OF STONE
REQUIRED

ISOMETRIC VIEW
OF KEYSTONE

SIDE
BEVEL

FIG. 223

STONE DOME
DETAIL OF KEYSTONE

CHAPTER XXI
SPIRAL OR TURRET STAIRCASE

FIGS. 224 and 225 show the plan and elevation of a spiral staircase connecting two floors. The staircase could be constructed in either stone or reinforced concrete; the latter material has been assumed and each step is a pre-cast unit. As the object in using such a staircase is to provide means of getting from one floor to the other in the least amount of space (known as the stair well), the proportion of the going to the tread is usually less than in the case of an ordinary staircase. The rise of the steps is also made steep to allow for headroom. The width of the steps is sometimes very narrow, as, for example, a stone spiral staircase at the Royal Naval College, Greenwich, where the width from wall to newel is about 1′ 3″.

It will be seen in Fig. 226 which shows a step unit turned upside down, that the steps includes part of the newel with a 1″ diameter hole for a reinforcement rod. The soffit of the step is carefully swept in shape and bearing joints are also formed. Fig. 227 shows the method of determining the joint between one step and another.

In drawing the plan and elevation of such a stair it is necessary to establish the position of the floor levels and to arrange for a number of steps that will allow a reasonable headroom, not less than 6′ 0″, and, if possible, about 9″ going on the walking line of each tread.

The setting up of the drawing follows the principles dealt with in Chapter XIV on the helix. Perpendicular ordinates from the steps about the wall line are produced to contact horizontal co-ordinates projected from the storey rod to find the positions of the steps in elevation. It will be seen that the front of each step is made tangent with the face of the newel to obtain the greatest possible strength.

The exact positions of the joints of the steps in elevation are obtained by developing the falling line of the steps about the wall, and projecting back to the elevation. Figs. 228 and 229 show a few steps developed about the wall face and the walking line respectively.

In forming any one of the steps it is necessary to construct a box containing the mould. The shuttering for the soffit of the step can be of plywood, bent to shape, and screwed down with

SPIRAL STAIRS

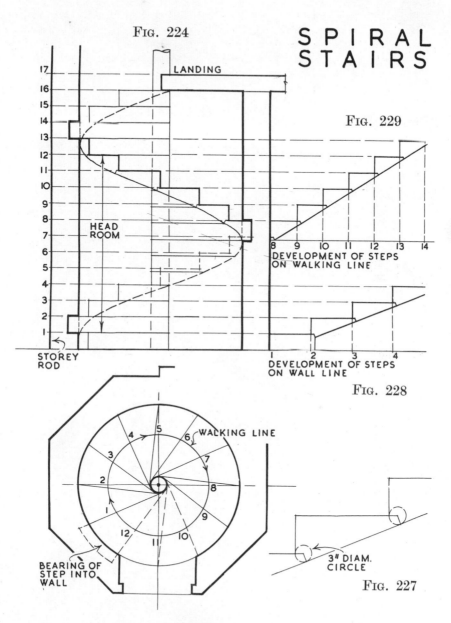

FIG. 224

LANDING

FIG. 229

17
16
15
14
13
12
11
10
9
8
7 HEAD ROOM
6
5
4
3
2
1

8 9 10 11 12 13 14
DEVELOPMENT OF STEPS ON WALKING LINE

STOREY ROD

1 2 3 4
DEVELOPMENT OF STEPS ON WALL LINE

FIG. 228

WALKING LINE

5
4   6
3   7
2   8
1   9
12 11 10

BEARING OF STEP INTO WALL

3" DIAM. CIRCLE

FIG. 227

FIG. 225

fixing fillets.   Figs. 230 and 231 gives the templets for the moulds, the same templets would apply if the steps were to be constructed of stone.

Figs. 232, 233 and 234 show the outline plans of other typical geometrical staircases.

PLATE IV

SPIRAL STAIRCASE FORMED OF PRE-CAST CONCRETE
UNITS SIMILAR TO THE STEPS SHOWN IN FIGS. 224-230.
THE LOWER PHOTOGRAPH SHOWS THE PRE-CAST
UNITS STACKED UPSIDE DOWN BEFORE BEING
PLACED IN POSITION

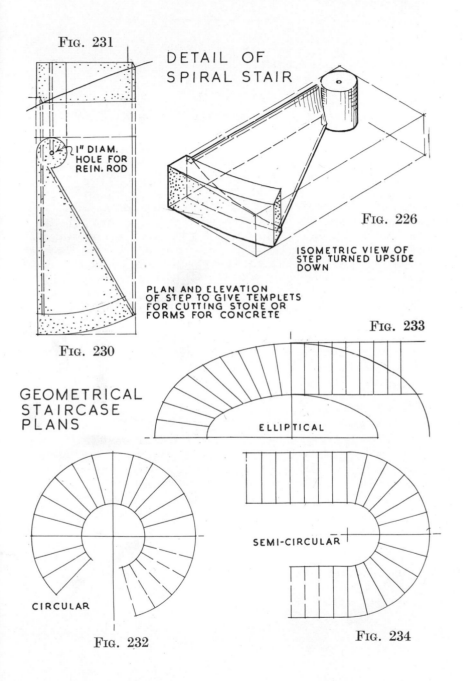

Fig. 231

DETAIL OF
SPIRAL STAIR

1" DIAM.
HOLE FOR
REIN. ROD

Fig. 226

ISOMETRIC VIEW OF
STEP TURNED UPSIDE
DOWN

PLAN AND ELEVATION
OF STEP TO GIVE TEMPLETS
FOR CUTTING STONE OR
FORMS FOR CONCRETE

Fig. 230

GEOMETRICAL
STAIRCASE
PLANS

Fig. 233

ELLIPTICAL

SEMI-CIRCULAR

CIRCULAR

Fig. 232

Fig. 234

CHAPTER XXII
LOUVRED VENTILATORS

Bull's-eye Ventilators

Figs. 235 and 236 show the elevation and section of a bull's-eye louvred ventilator constructed in wood. The circular frame is made of four shaped units, $4'' \times 3''$, joined together by handrail bolts and wood dowels or hammer-head key joints. The louvres are $\frac{3}{4}''$ thick, inclined at a reasonable angle, and housed into the frame $\frac{1}{2}''$ deep.

To find the shapes of the louvres it is necessary to obtain top and bottom face moulds for each louvre. As the top and bottom face of any louvre can be represented by a cut taken through a cylinder so as to give an ellipse, then the ellipse must first be found. Fig. 237 shows how it is projected from the elevation or section of the frame, and gives the top and bottom face moulds for the third louvre. Horizontal ordinates are projected from A and C and the major axis is drawn parallel to the inclination of the louvres, the minor axis B^1D^1 is equal the distance BD in the elevation. For the face moulds horizontal ordinates are projected to the major axis A^1C^1 from index points 1, 2, 3, 4 on the section, and then produced at right-angles to the axis to the outline of the ellipse, as shown.

Fig. 238 shows an isometric view of the selected louvre as it would be transformed from a piece of wood. The pitch bevel regulates the positions of the top and bottom face moulds.

Fig. 239 shows an isometric view of the circular frame within a square frame used for the purpose of marking off the cuts for housing the louvres. The positions of the cuts as given by the section, Fig. 236, are set out on opposite sides of the square frame and then by using a straight-edge markings for the cuts can be made on both faces of the circular frame. The geometrical method of marking these cuts would be to develop a falling mould which which be equal to the circumference of the inner face of the frame. However, although this theory may be applied, the result may be uncertain owing to the preparation of the frame.

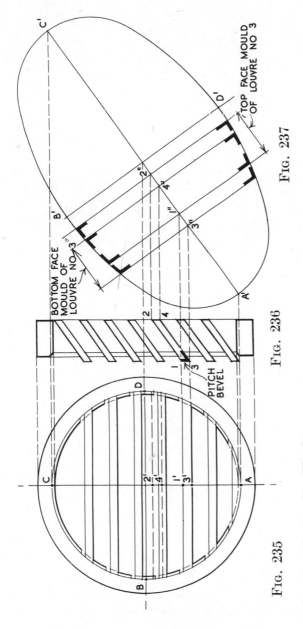

BOTTOM FACE MOULD OF LOUVRE NO 3

TOP FACE MOULD OF LOUVRE NO 3

PITCH BEVEL

Fɪɢ. 235

Fɪɢ. 236

Fɪɢ. 237

LOUVRED
VENTILATOR
BULLS EYE

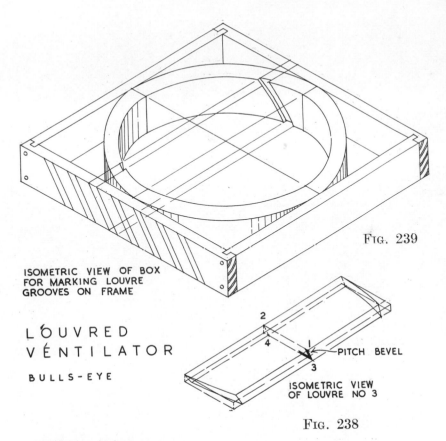

FIG. 239

ISOMETRIC VIEW OF BOX
FOR MARKING LOUVRE
GROOVES ON FRAME

LOUVRED
VENTILATOR

BULLS-EYE

PITCH BEVEL

ISOMETRIC VIEW
OF LOUVRE NO 3

FIG. 238

Triangular Ventilator

Figs. 240 and 241 show the elevation and section of an equilateral triangular louvred ventilator. The frame is made of $4\frac{1}{2}'' \times 1\frac{1}{2}''$ timber jointed at the corners. The louvres are $\frac{3}{4}''$ thick, inclined at a suitable angle, and housed into the frame $\frac{1}{2}''$ deep. The face moulds are obtained in a similar manner to the previous example, as seen in Fig. 242. Horizontal ordinates are projected from A and B to the line $A''B''$ which is parallel to the inclination of the louvres. $C''D''$ equal to C^1D^1 is drawn at right-angles to $A''B''$ through A'', C'' and D'' are joined to B''. Horizontal lines are then projected from points 1, 2, 3, 4 on the section to line $A''B''$, and then produced at right-angles to $C''B''$ and $D''B''$ to find the face moulds of the third louvre.

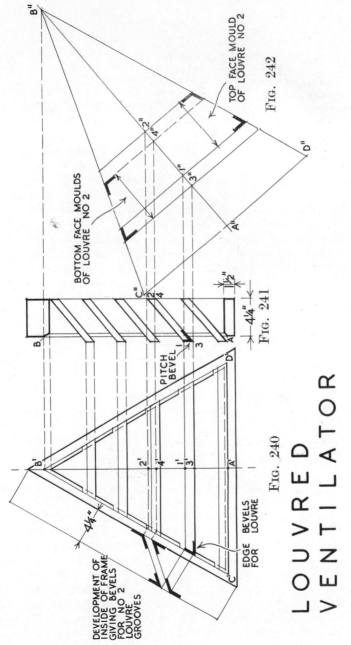

BOTTOM FACE MOULDS
OF LOUVRE NO 2

TOP FACE MOULD
OF LOUVRE NO 2

FIG. 242

PITCH
BEVEL

FIG. 241

DEVELOPMENT OF
INSIDE OF FRAME
GIVING BEVELS
FOR NO 2
LOUVRE
GROOVES

EDGE BEVELS
FOR LOUVRE

FIG. 240

LOUVRED
VENTILATOR
TRIANGULAR

CHAPTER XXIII
SPLAYED WOOD LININGS

FIGS. 243 to 245 show the plan, part elevation, and section of a splayed wood lining fitting to a casement window frame. The wood lining consists of $1\frac{1}{4}''$ styles, rails, and muntins, with $\frac{1}{4}''$ panels. The head and jamb linings are splayed and tongued together. It is necessary to obtain the true shapes of the linings and panels with their bevels.

The styles must be shaped from squared sections as seen in plan, Fig. 243, and indexed 1 and 2. The edge bevel which will give the required splayed section is also seen.

The shapes of the linings are found by inclined plane projection. With centre 1 and radius 1, 2 an arc is described to the horizontal projection of 1 and a perpendicular ordinate is projected to contact the horizontal co-ordinate 2^1 to find the jamb lining. The head lining is found in a similar manner by inclined plane projection from the section.

Figs. 246 to 250 give the views and working details of a semi-circular-headed splayed panelled lining. This type of wood lining may be made of solid timbers for the built-up styles or the styles may be made of thin strips of timber bent and glued together over a shaped cradle.

Figs. 246 to 248 show the plan, elevation and section of such a panelled lining, the styles of which are shaped from solid timber, the panels being plywood.

The method of obtaining the templets, bevels, sizes of timber, etc., is shown in Figs. 246 and 247. Fig. 249 gives an isometric view of the front style which appears to be resting on a half cone, and Fig. 250 gives an isometric view of a portion of this style with sizes, bevels, etc.

The working bevels and face moulds are obtained as follows: The plan, elevation and section are drawn. The plan, Fig. 246, shows the thickness of timber for the front style together with edge bevel "C," and pitch bevel "D." Fig. 247 shows the length and width of timber with end bevels "A^1" and "B^1," also the front and back face moulds. The face moulds are obtained by projecting from the plan the indexed points, 1, 2, 3 and 4 to the springing line in elevation. With centre R^1 arcs are described from 1 and 2 and 3 and 4 to the joint lines of the styles.

These face moulds are arranged on each side of the squared-up timber with adjustment bevels as seen in Fig. 250.

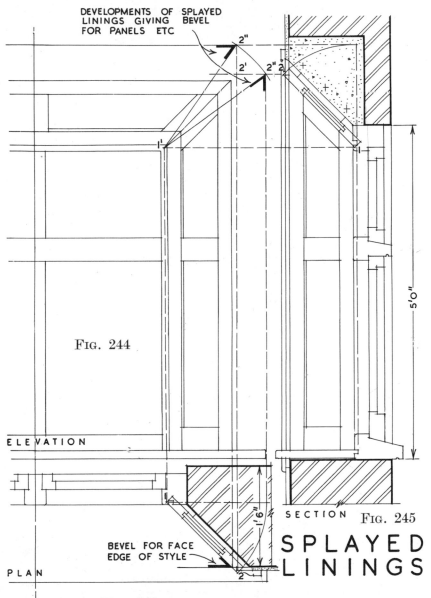

DEVELOPMENTS OF SPLAYED
LININGS GIVING BEVEL
FOR PANELS ETC

2"

2'

2" 2"

1'

5'0"

Fig. 244

ELEVATION

1'6"

SECTION   Fig. 245

BEVEL FOR FACE
EDGE OF STYLE

PLAN

2"

SPLAYED LININGS

Fig. 243

Fig. 246 shows how the splayed panels are found, also the shapes of developed laminated strips which are used to build up the styles in the alternative process.

The shapes of panels are obtained by describing arcs with centre R and radii the width of panel in section on plan, and marking along the appropriate arc distances corresponding to AB and CD as in the elevation.

The developed laminated strips are obtained by describing arcs, centre R as before, from 2 and 4 on plan section, to the proposed joints.

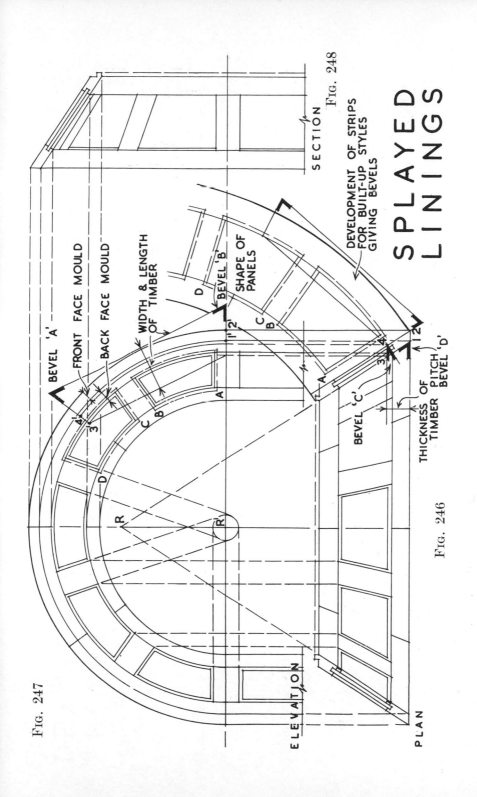

FIG. 248

SECTION

DEVELOPMENT OF STRIPS
FOR BUILT-UP STYLES
GIVING BEVELS

SPLAYED
LININGS

BEVEL 'A'

FRONT FACE MOULD

BACK FACE MOULD

WIDTH & LENGTH
OF TIMBER

BEVEL 'B'

SHAPE OF
PANELS

BEVEL 'C'

THICKNESS OF
TIMBER

PITCH
BEVEL 'D'

FIG. 247

FIG. 246

R

ELEVATION

PLAN

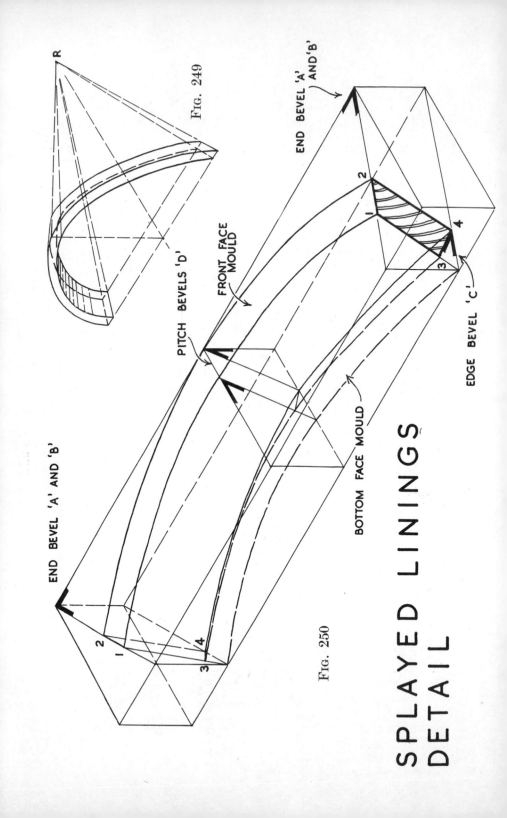

R

FIG. 249

END BEVEL 'A' AND 'B'

PITCH BEVELS 'D'

FRONT FACE MOULD

END BEVEL 'A' AND 'B'

2
1
4
3

FIG. 250

BOTTOM FACE MOULD

EDGE BEVEL 'C'

2
1
4
3

SPLAYED LININGS
DETAIL

CHAPTER XXIV
ROOF BEVELS

GEOMETRICAL drawing is seldom employed at the present day for finding roof bevels, as the steel roofing square, which gives the tables of the various cuts and lengths of roofing members is far more quickly applied in practice. The following description, however, will enable the student to see how the cuts and surface developments are obtained, as well as being a satisfactory practical method. It is also of value to the quantity surveyor in estimating.

Single Purlin Hipped Roof

Figs. 251 to 256 give all the information necessary needed to cut a hipped purlin roof. The roof consists of surfaces of equal pitch, which is 45 degrees—known as $\frac{1}{2}$ pitch or square pitch.

Fig. 251 shows the plan and elevation of the roof with a gable end, three hip rafters and one valley rafter.

Fig. 252 describes a rafter fitting against a wall-plate and ridge, with the plate cut and plumb cut respectively indicated.

The bevels and length of a common rafter are $H^1\!\!-\!A^1B^1$, as seen in Fig. 251.

The bevels and length of hip rafter FG are obtained by projecting perpendicular to FG on plan the rise to G^3. Similar method is used for the other hip rafters.

The bevels and length of valley rafter DH is obtained by projecting perpendicular to DH on plan the rise to H^3.

The bevels of the jack rafters, which have an oblique cut at the top where contact is made with the hip rafters, are found in the case of jack rafter LK. The plumb cut and plate cut with length of rafter are seen in elevation L^1K^1. The cross cut is found by projecting the length of the rafter to the developed surface of the roof A, B, H^2, J^2, the cut being L^2.

The bevels of the cripple jack rafters, which make contact with the ridge and the valley rafter are found as in the case of cripple jack rafter OP, the plumb cut and foot cut and the length of which are seen in the elevation O^1P^1. The cross cut is found by projecting the length of the rafter to the developed surface C^2D^2HJ, the cut being O^2.

Fig. 253 shows how the cross cuts can be found by an alternative method. The plan of the hip or valley rafter is drawn to show the jack rafters. Above the plan is drawn the elevation of the

173

jack rafters to give views of the oblique cuts, the surface AB is developed and A^2B^1 is the cross cut bevel.

Fig. 254 shows the views of the various roof members intersecting the ridge. The cuts of these members are found on the developed surfaces of the roof, e.g. hip rafters EG and FG—the cross cut bevels are at G^2.

Angle of Backing of Hip Rafter

This is known as the dihedral angle between the roof planes. Fig. 255 gives the roof planes $AFGH$ and EFG. Any line ST perpendicular to FG^3 is drawn, and with centre S and radius ST an arc is described to the horizontal plane to give T^1. A line perpendicular to FG is drawn through S to contact the traces of planes, i.e. wall-plates. From the points of contact lines are drawn to T^1 giving the required angle. Also, in this figure is seen the application of the bevel to the hip rafter.

Bevels of Purlins against Hip and Valley Rafters

Fig. 256 gives the plan and sectional elevation of the purlin against hip rafter EG. A^1B^1 is the top cut and C^1B^1 the side cut. The top bevel is found by describing an arc with centre B and radius BA to the horizontal at B, and projecting a perpendicular ordinate to contact the horizontal co-ordinate from A^1 to give A^2, which is joined to B^1. The side bevel is found in a similar manner.

Broach Spire

Figs. 257 to 259 describe the application of geometry to a broach spire, which is formed by an octagonal pyramid penetrating a square pyramid. The plan and elevation must be drawn before the bevels can be found. The proportions of the two pyramids having been determined—the square pyramid is usually pitched at 60 degrees—the outline plan and elevation are drawn. A new elevation is necessary in order to find where the hip rafters of the square pyramid make contact with the planes of the octagonal pyramid. When so found, the points of contact, such as M^2 and K^2 can be projected back to the plan to complete it and also the elevation.

The developed surfaces of the roof are found as shown in the diagram.

Fig. 258 gives the dihedral angle of the hip rafters for the octagonal pyramid.

Fig. 259 shows the jointing where the hip rafters meet an octagonal mast at the apex.

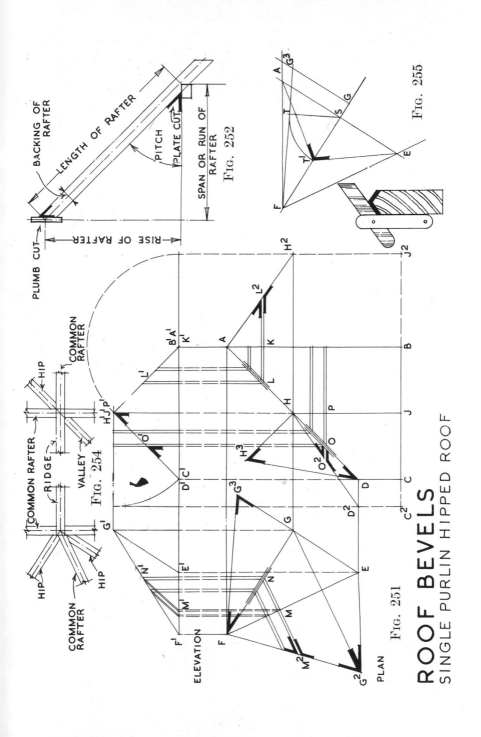

BACKING OF RAFTER

LENGTH OF RAFTER

PITCH

PLATE CUT

SPAN OR RUN OF RAFTER

FIG. 252

PLUMB CUT

RISE OF RAFTER

FIG. 255

COMMON RAFTER

HIP

COMMON RAFTER

RIDGE

VALLEY

FIG. 254

HIP

HIP

COMMON RAFTER

ELEVATION

PLAN

FIG. 251

ROOF BEVELS
SINGLE PURLIN HIPPED ROOF

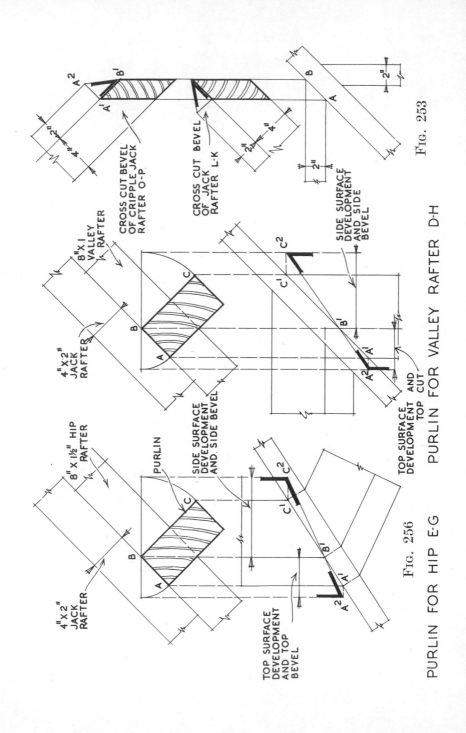

CROSS CUT BEVEL OF CRIPPLE JACK RAFTER O-P

CROSS CUT BEVEL OF JACK RAFTER L-K

SIDE SURFACE DEVELOPMENT AND SIDE BEVEL

2"

2"

4"

4"

2"

4"

2"

A²

B'

A'

A

B

FIG. 253

8" X 1 VALLEY RAFTER

4" X 2" JACK RAFTER

SIDE SURFACE DEVELOPMENT AND SIDE BEVEL

TOP SURFACE DEVELOPMENT AND TOP CUT

PURLIN FOR VALLEY RAFTER D-H

8" X 1½" HIP RAFTER

PURLIN

4" X 2" JACK RAFTER

SIDE SURFACE DEVELOPMENT AND SIDE BEVEL

TOP SURFACE DEVELOPMENT AND TOP BEVEL

FIG. 256

PURLIN FOR HIP E-G

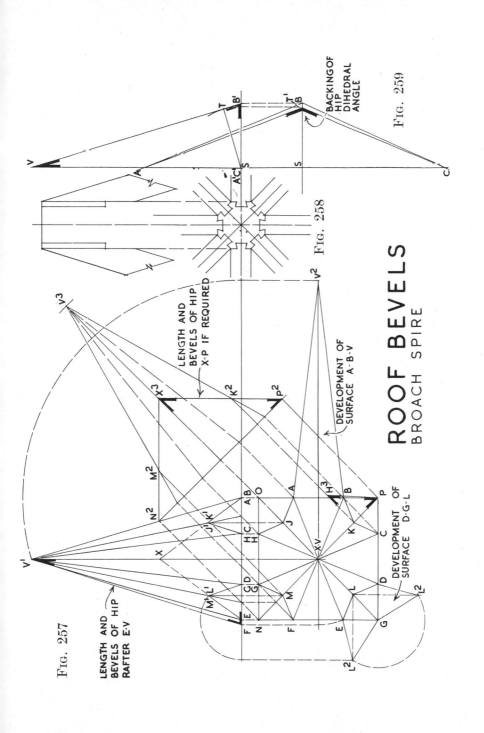

ROOF BEVELS
BROACH SPIRE

Fig. 257

LENGTH AND
BEVELS OF HIP
RAFTER E-V

LENGTH AND
BEVELS OF HIP
X-P IF REQUIRED

DEVELOPMENT OF
SURFACE A-B-V

DEVELOPMENT OF
SURFACE D-G-L

Fig. 258

Fig. 259

BACKING OF
HIP
DIHEDRAL
ANGLE

CHAPTER XXV

CIRCLE ON CIRCLE ARCHES AND FRAMING

CIRCLE on circle (or double curvature) is the term used to describe the condition of objects which in both plan and elevation are seen to be wholly or partly circular, elliptical, or otherwise curved.

Fig. 260 shows a half cylinder in plan and elevation with a strip falling over the surface. It will be seen that this strip appears segmental in plan and semi-circular in elevation. This figure also shows the development of the strip, which is known as a falling mould. The development is obtained by plotting the circumference of the semi-circle, in twelve equal lengths, indexed 0′ to 12′ in plan, along a dimension line, indexed 0″ to 12″, which is perpendicular to the axis of the cylinder. Perpendicular ordinates are projected from 0″ to 12″ to contact horizontally projected co-ordinates from the plan of the strip.

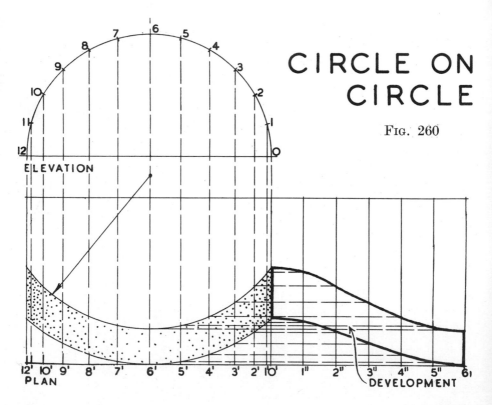

CIRCLE ON CIRCLE

FIG. 260

ELEVATION

PLAN

DEVELOPMENT

Figs. 261 and 262 show a conoid with a strip falling over the surface. The conoid is seen as a triangle in plan and a semi-circle in elevation. The front of the conoid is equal in height to the back, therefore if the elevation is a semi-circle by lengthening or shortening the figure the front will become a semi-ellipse.

RP is the length of the conoid and X the radius of the semi-circular front. It is impossible to develop accurately the surface of the conoid, but the following describes the nearest approximation. The semi-circle of the front in elevation is divided into 12 equal parts, indexed 0 to 12, which are projected to the plan, indexed 0' to 12'. Chords are drawn on the elevation: 1. 11, 2. 10, 3. 9, 4. 8, 5. 7, cutting the vertical axis at A, B, C, D and E respectively. Point 6 is also indexed F. Taking the unit of the conoid $R\,A01$; $R\,A'$ is drawn perpendicular to $R0'$. With centre A' and radius $R1'$ an arc is described to cut another arc struck from centre 0' with radius equal to the chord 0.1, the intersection giving point $1''$ and $R\,A'0'1''$ is the development of the unit. Other units can be developed on similar lines, as shown in the drawing.

The falling mould of the strip is obtained by plotting on dimension lines $R'0'$ to $F'6''$ the radius of the strip as seen in plan.

Figs. 263 and 264 show a conoidal arch constructed in stone. Fig. 265 gives a pictorial view of the solid form of the arch based upon two conoids, one for the intrados and the other for the extrados. The conoids are parallel. It is usual to make the front of the intrados semi-circular in elevation, in which case the front of the extrados and the back of intrados appear as semi-ellipses, as shown in the drawing.

Fig. 263 gives the plan of the two conoids and the plan of the wall supporting the arch. $CDEF$ represents the thickness and depth of the arch.

It will be realised that the radiant joint lines of the arch are helical lines, and that the joints along the intrados and extrados are horizontal lines in elevation.

To divide the extrados into equal units for joints, the segment FG in plan must be developed out straight in elevation by the method described in Fig. 45, Chapter IV.

Fig. 265 shows how the helical lines are obtained. The joint, indexed 1.2., between the springer stone and the first voussoir, which in theory radiates to P is divided vertically into two equal parts, to give W. Points 1 and 2 are projected to the plan to give points 1^1 and 2^1 on the face of the arch. The distance $1^1.2^1$ is divided into two equal parts to give W^1. Where W^1 produced vertically intersects a horizontal from W an intermediate point is found for the helical line.

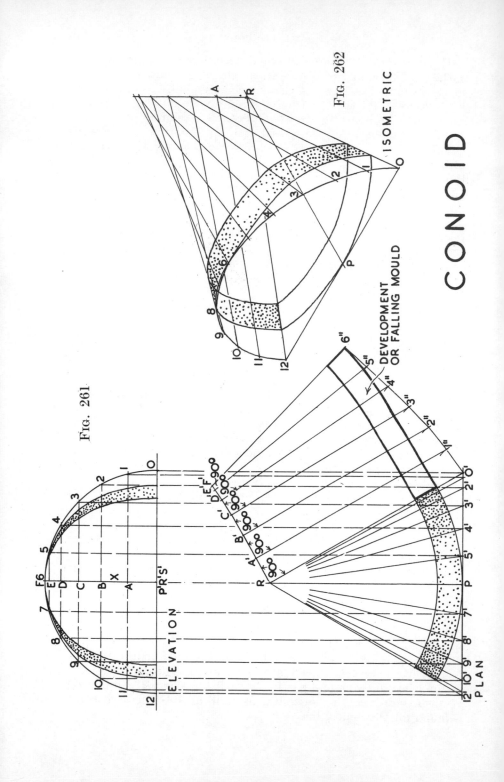

Fig. 262

ISOMETRIC

DEVELOPMENT
OR FALLING MOULD

Fig. 261

ELEVATION

PLAN

CONOID

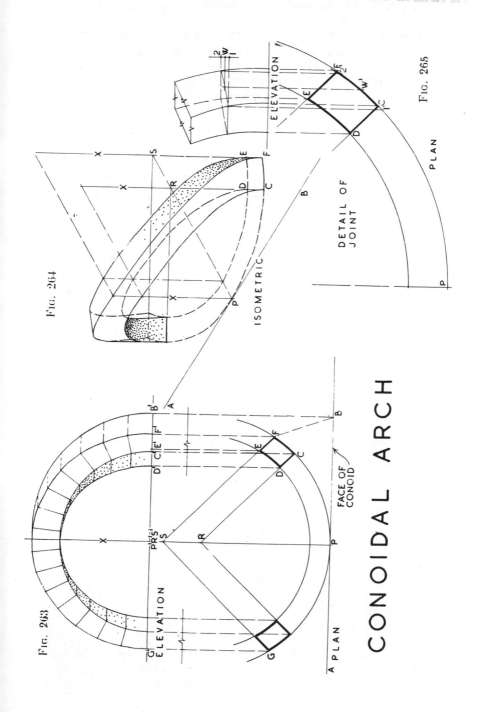

Fig. 263

Fig. 264

Fig. 265

ELEVATION

ISOMETRIC

DETAIL OF JOINT

PLAN

ELEVATION

FACE OF CONOID

PLAN

CONOIDAL ARCH

Circle on Circle Wood Door Frame with Parallel Jambs

Fig. 266 shows the complete setting out for this frame which is based on the theory illustrated in Fig. 260 (the cylinder).

Although costly in material it is general practice to make this type of frame out of solid units of timber, two or three pieces being used according to size. In this example two pieces of timber are used. If the outside of the frame is made semi-circular in elevation then the inside face is semi-elliptical.

The thickness of timber needed for the frame is found in plan by means of a chord and parallel tangent to the joints as shown. Fig. 267 shows a pictorial view of the shape of timber required. Two face moulds are required to enable the cutting to shape to be made. These face moulds, which are equal, are found by dividing the outside edge of the frame into, say, twelve equal parts, from which perpendicular ordinates are projected to the front and back faces of the timber in plan, so that a new elevation with O^1R^{11} as the $X-Y$ line can be obtained.

By applying the front and back face moulds on the timber with the aid of the bevels indicated in the drawing the part hollow cylinder can be cut to shape. (Note: Before the top bevel can be applied the piece of timber must be cut off horizontally.)

To form the double curvature it is necessary to obtain internal and external falling moulds of the frame for application to the shaped timber, as seen in Fig. 267.

Fig. 268 illustrates a photograph of this piece of joinery. Each joint may be formed either by handrail bolts and dowels or hammer-headed key joints.

Circle on Circle Wood Door Frame with Radiating Joints

Fig. 269 gives the complete setting out for this frame based on the theory illustrated in Figs. 261 and 262 (the conoid).

Although the method of constructing the frame is similar to that of the previous example, it is much more difficult to set out and make. It is, however, considered to be of better appearance.

In setting out the frame, the plan and elevation are drawn, usually with the outside of the frame forming a semi-circle in elevation. The thickness of the timber is obtained by means of a chord and parallel tangent to the joints in plan. The face moulds, which in this case are not equal in shape, are obtained by dividing the top front edge of the frame into a number of equal parts, ten in the drawing, from which perpendicular ordinates are projected to the plan of the frame. For the front face mould a new elevation is obtained of the front of the frame, using O^1P^1 as the new $X-Y$ line and by producing the projected points on the frame radial from R^1 to O^1P^1 and thence perpendicular

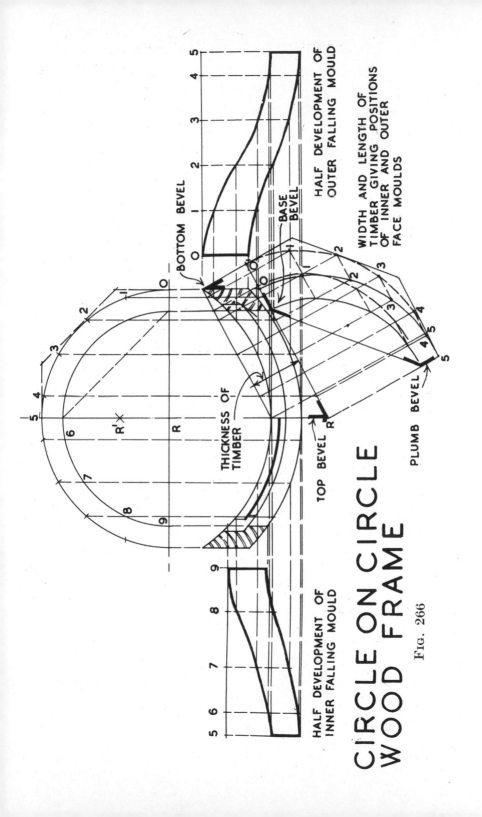

BOTTOM BEVEL

HALF DEVELOPMENT OF
OUTER FALLING MOULD

BASE BEVEL

WIDTH AND LENGTH OF
TIMBER GIVING POSITIONS
OF INNER AND OUTER
FACE MOULDS

THICKNESS OF
TIMBER

R'

R

TOP BEVEL

PLUMB BEVEL

HALF DEVELOPMENT OF
INNER FALLING MOULD

CIRCLE ON CIRCLE
WOOD FRAME

FIG. 266

to O^1P^1. The inside face mould is obtained from corresponding indexed points on the inside face of the frame in elevation projected as perpendicular ordinates to the same face on plan, radiated back to R^1. Where the ordinates intersect the chord S^1T perpendicular lines are projected for the new elevation.

The length and width of the timber are found by projecting from S in plan to locate the base bevel.

Before applying the face moulds to the timber the bevels will have to be arranged, the timber being first cut at the top and bottom. When the moulds are set in position and the inside and top faces of the timber are shaped, falling moulds will be needed to mark the segment in plan. The method of finding these falling moulds has already been explained in Fig. 261.

Fig. 270 illustrates a photograph of this type of frame in progress—one-half completed, the other half with falling moulds set for marking.

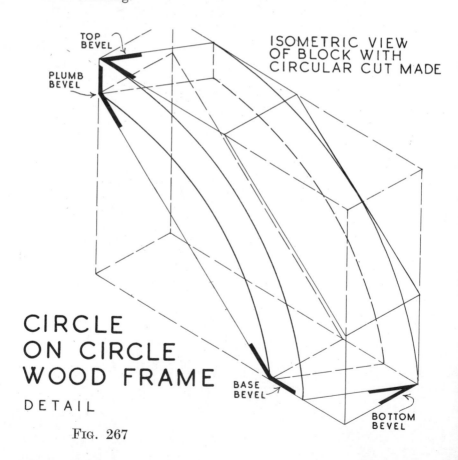

TOP BEVEL
PLUMB BEVEL
ISOMETRIC VIEW OF BLOCK WITH CIRCULAR CUT MADE
BASE BEVEL
BOTTOM BEVEL

CIRCLE ON CIRCLE WOOD FRAME

DETAIL

FIG. 267

PLATE V

FIG. 268. ACTUAL EXAMPLE OF CIRCLE ON CIRCLE
WOOD FRAME WITH PARALLEL JAMBS. THE CURVE
OF THE BASE BOARD CORRESPONDS TO THE CURVE
OF THE HEAD OF THE FRAME ON PLAN

PLATE VI

FIG. 270. ACTUAL EXAMPLE OF CIRCLE ON CIRCLE WOOD
FRAME WITH RADIATING JOINTS WITH ONE HALF COMPLETED
AND THE OTHER HALF WITH FALLING MOULDS SET IN POSITION

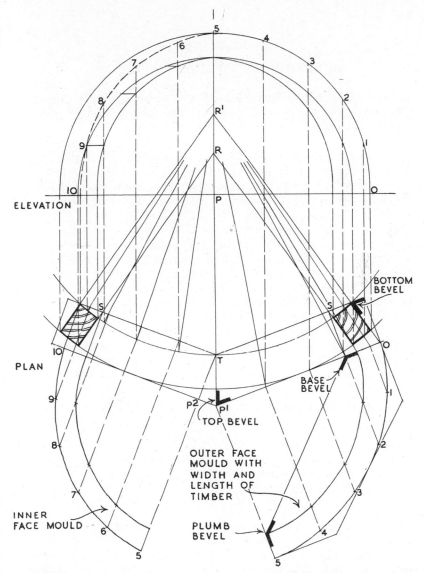

ELEVATION

PLAN

R¹

R

P

5
6
7
8
9
10

4
3
2
1
O

S

S

BOTTOM
BEVEL

10

T

O

9

P2   P¹
TOP BEVEL

1

BASE
BEVEL

8

2

7

OUTER FACE
MOULD WITH
WIDTH AND
LENGTH OF
TIMBER

3

INNER
FACE MOULD

6

5

PLUMB
BEVEL

4

5

CIRCLE ON CIRCLE WOOD FRAME

Fig. 269

CHAPTER XXVI

THE THEORY OF HANDRAILING

The theory of handrailing is dealt with briefly in this chapter, as the subject is a very comprehensive one, and it is only possible here to give examples of some of the usual types.

Handrails can, of course, be made by "rule of thumb" by cutting the required shapes from large sections of timber, but the method is wasteful and should never be used. Methods as described in the following pages should be employed, giving satisfactory results with accuracy and economy of material and labour.

A good grasp of plane geometry is essential as a foundation for the understanding of the principles, and the student is advised to make models to help the visualisation of the shapes involved, unless practical work is being undertaken at the same time.

Fig. 271 shows a hollow cylinder cut by a plane. It will be seen that the inner and outer curves will represent a face mould which would be applied to the block forming the wreath.

Fig. 272 shows the centre line of a handrail over the quadrant of a spiral staircase. It will be realised that such a line rises in proportion with the rise of each step and consequently the course of the rail follows the line of the nosings of the treads.

The Tangent Helical Joint at Springing Point System

This is a useful method for the following cases:

(1) Spiral staircase.
(2) Quarter-space of winders connecting two straight flights.
(3) Half-space of winders.
(4) Half-space landing.
(5) The scroll.

Spiral Staircase. Fig. 273 shows the setting out of the wreath for a quarter turn of three winders for a spiral staircase. A and C are the joint lines on the centre line, and the rise is equal to three risers (say 1' 9"). The tangents AB and BC are drawn on plan and are developed to the elevation. By referring to Fig. 272, it will be seen how these tangents rule the traces of the oblique plane.

To obtain the face mould a new plan is projected of AC complete with tangents $A^2B^2C^2$. Note that the joint lines on the face moulds are at right-angles to the tangents. The application of the face mould on the plank is illustrated in Figs. 275,

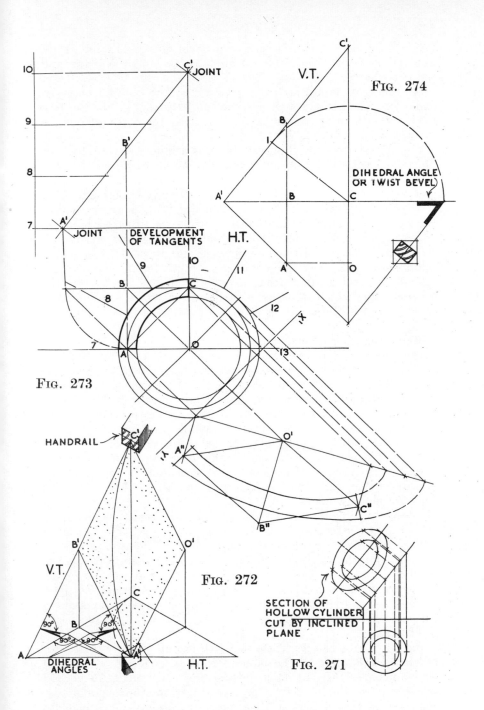

10

9

8

7 A' JOINT

DEVELOPMENT OF TANGENTS

C' JOINT

B'

V.T.

FIG. 274

DIHEDRAL ANGLE OR TWIST BEVEL

H.T.

9

8

7

B

C

A O

10

11

12

13

FIG. 273

HANDRAIL

C'

A"

Y

O'

C"

B"

B'

O'

V.T.

C

B

A

90° 90°

90° 90°

A'

DIHEDRAL ANGLES

H.T.

FIG. 272

SECTION OF HOLLOW CYLINDER CUT BY INCLINED PLANE

FIG. 271

276, 277 and 278, but first, the twist bevel must be found. Figs.
274 and 275 show the dihedral angle of the oblique plane and
the twist bevel.

As the face mould is the impression of the oblique plane, it
has reference only through the centre of the plank and the face
mould has therefore to be applied on both the top and bottom
surfaces.

Fig. 275 shows how the twist bevel is applied on the block; it
must be reversed at the opposite end. It will be noted that the
width of the timber at the ends of the block must be a little
greater than the face mould for reasons already explained.

The next operation is illustrated in Fig. 276. Having applied
the bevels and marked the setting out of the squared handrail
on each end of the block, the tangent markings are reproduced
by the adjustment of the face moulds and by markings on the
plumb bevel. As the tangents on the cylinder in plan form a
straight line when developed, the falling line of the handrail is
a helical line, which when developed is a straight line. Therefore
there is no need for a falling mould to obtain the finished wreath,
as seen in Fig. 278.

Half-space of Winders. Figs. 279 and 280 illustrate the setting
out of a handrail suitable for a half space of six winders connecting
two straight flights, the method being the same as in the previous
case. The wreaths form a helical curve, therefore the easements
from the straight flights to the wreaths are formed on the straight
rails either by gluing on pieces of wood on the top and bottom,
or by joining on extra sections. To avoid an ill-conditioned rail
it is advisable to set back the third and last riser of the first flight
and the first riser of the second flight from the springing line of
the wreaths so that the easements can be arranged over the risers.
It will be seen that the rise of the wreaths is a little less than
that of the six winders.

The arrangements for the shaping of the wreaths is the same
as in the previous case.

Fig. 281 illustrates how the outer face of the string can be
obtained for the same six-winder staircase. Having set out the
winders in plan projections from the storey rod can be made.
To connect the straight flights with the bent string the angles
are bisected so that suitable centres can be determined for striking
the arcs of easement. (Note the line the handrail makes with
the treads.)

Figs. 282 and 283 illustrate the setting out of the wreaths for
a half-space landing by the same method as used before, also the
development of the centre line of the string. Although the method
is quite a practical one for this case, the results are thought by
some to be unsatisfactory in appearance and inconvenient for

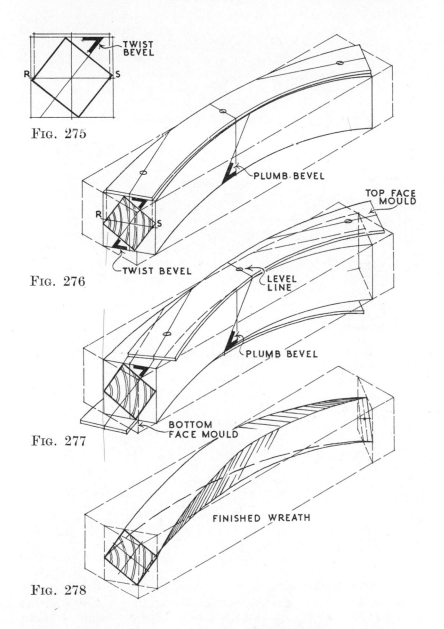

Fig. 275

TWIST BEVEL

R S

PLUMB·BEVEL

Fig. 276

TWIST BEVEL

R S

TOP FACE MOULD

LEVEL LINE

Fig. 277

PLUMB BEVEL

BOTTOM FACE MOULD

FINISHED WREATH

Fig. 278

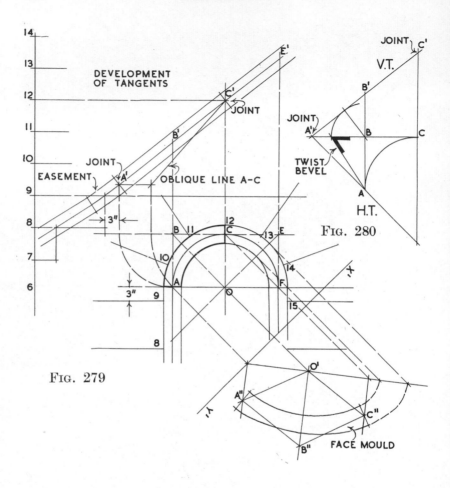

FIG. 279

FIG. 280

handling when walking from one flight to the other. An alternative method is described later.

Scroll Over Curtail Step

Figs. 284, 285 and 286 illustrate the setting out of a wreath completing a scroll over a curtail step. The procedure is briefly as follows: The plan of the required scroll is drawn by any of the methods previously described (Chapter V). The tangents and the plan containing the centre of the string are developed. Almost always the scroll is arranged half a riser higher than the rest of

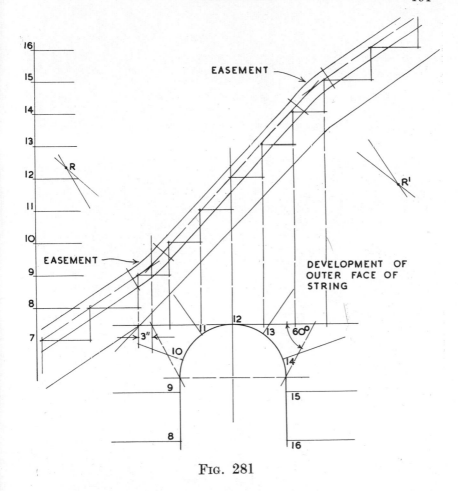

FIG. 281

the handrail, and consequently the pitch will alter. The easements are arranged as follows: (1) The easement on the block from EC —as DC is the horizontal tangent and CD the inclined tangent, then the pitch from DE to C is an inclined plane. The pitch bevel to unite the wreath is seen at C and shown also in Fig. 286. (2) The easement connecting the wreath and the straight flight is as in previous cases arranged on the straight rail.

Fig. 284 illustrates the method of finding the face mould for the wreath. The twist bevel is also shown.

Fig. 285 illustrates the method of finding the falling mould which is needed for application on the block for easement CE.

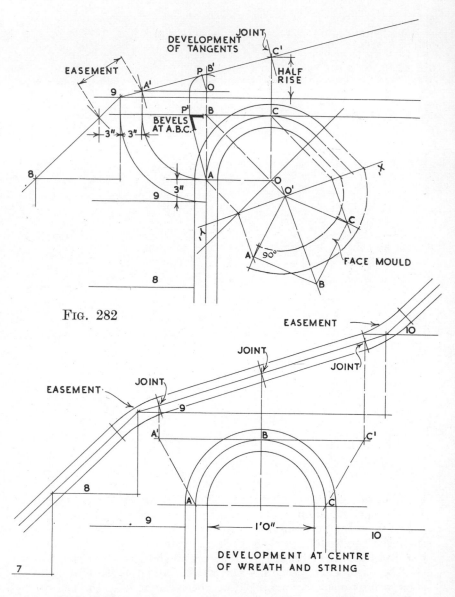

JOINT

DEVELOPMENT
OF TANGENTS

EASEMENT

9

A'

P B'

O

C'

HALF
RISE

P' B

BEVELS
AT A.B.C.

B

C

3" 3"

8

9 3"

A

O

O'

C

-Y

90°

A

FACE MOULD

B

8

FIG. 282

EASEMENT

10

JOINT

JOINT

EASEMENT

JOINT

A'

B

C'

9

8

A

C

7

9

1'0"

10

DEVELOPMENT AT CENTRE
OF WREATH AND STRING

FIG. 283

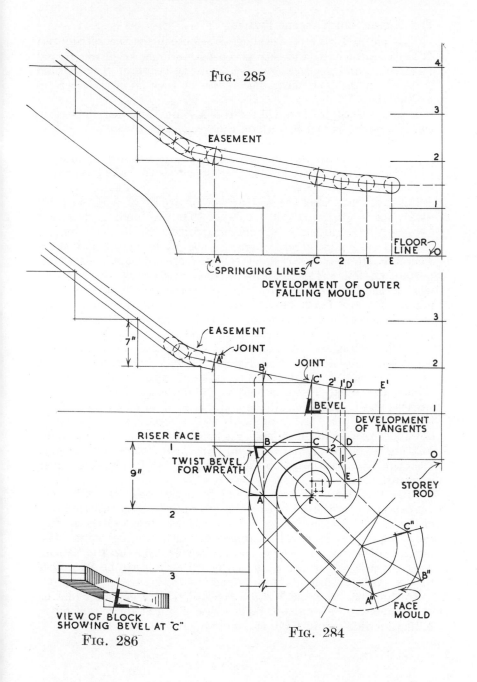

FIG. 285

EASEMENT

A ⌐C 2 1 E
⌐SPRINGING LINES

DEVELOPMENT OF OUTER
FALLING MOULD

FLOOR
LINE

4

3

2

1

0

EASEMENT
JOINT

7"

A'

B'

JOINT
C' 2' 1'D' E'
BEVEL

DEVELOPMENT
OF TANGENTS

3

2

1

RISER FACE
1

TWIST BEVEL
FOR WREATH

9"

2

3

B C 2 D
2
1
A
E
F

STOREY
ROD

0

C"

B"

A"
FACE
MOULD

VIEW OF BLOCK
SHOWING BEVEL AT "C"

FIG. 286

FIG. 284

The Square Cut Tangent System

This method may prove more satisfactory for the setting out of wreaths for half- and quarter-space landings. It gives a good appearance and good easements about the landing. The method is based on the inclined plane, as can be seen from the diagram in Fig. 288.

It is advisable to arrange for the easements to be effected on the straight rails rather than on the wreaths or trouble in cutting and adjusting the joints may be encountered. Long shanks are advisable for small wells to overcome the possibility of an awkward appearance at the joints. A good rule is to make the shanks half the width of the tread.

Fig. 287 illustrates the setting out of a pair of wreaths for a half-space landing. It will be noted that the landing risers are half the going distance of tangent points BD—this being of course a previous arrangement in the planning of the stair. Therefore, tangents AB and BC, etc., are all equal. It is important to follow this practice otherwise the resulting handrail will be unbalanced. If, however, for some reason or other the flights of stairs finish beyond the springing lines then the two rails will have to be moved, the top rail being ramped up and the lower rail ramped down until the centres are level.

In the setting out of the wreaths in Fig. 287 the plan of the wreaths is drawn with the tangents through the centre lines at A B C D and E. Projections are made to the elevation so that C^1 is equal to half a riser in height. A^1B^1 being the pitch of the wreaths this distance is half the major axis of an ellipse and B^1C^1 is half the minor axis. From this the face mould can be easily obtained. An addition in length is made by adding the shank for jointing to the straight rails. Only one face mould is necessary, although two are shown in Figs. 290 and 291 to illustrate their application.

After the block has been cut out from timber of the thickness as seen in Fig. 289, the twist bevel is applied at the squared end of the block. As the face mould governs the centre of the timber the pitch or plumb bevel is applied at the springing point. The face mould is then adjusted to suit the bevels. The top and bottom faces of the block having been marked, the sides can be shaped so that a parallel thickness is obtained.

To shape the top and bottom faces of the wreaths is a matter of judgment by eye, although in cases of doubt inner and outer falling moulds would have to be obtained.

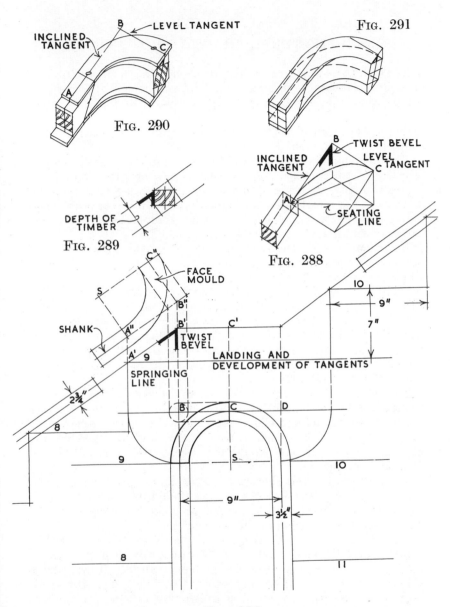

INCLINED TANGENT

B — LEVEL TANGENT

C

A

FIG. 290

FIG. 291

DEPTH OF TIMBER

FIG. 289

TWIST BEVEL

INCLINED TANGENT

LEVEL TANGENT

B

C

A

SEATING LINE

FIG. 288

C"

FACE MOULD

S

B"

SHANK

A"

B'

C'

A' 9

TWIST BEVEL

10

9"

7"

SPRINGING LINE

LANDING AND DEVELOPMENT OF TANGENTS

2¾"

8

B   C   D

9   S   10

9"   3½"

8   11

FIG 287

CHAPTER XXVII
ARCHITECTURAL SHADOW PROJECTION

Shades and shadows are indicated on drawings principally as a means of expressing more fully the three-dimensional forms and the relationships of various planes of objects or buildings than can be shown in a line drawing alone. They help to give a more realistic appearance without sacrificing the advantages of a geometrical projection.

The following definitions should be borne in mind: (1) a shadow falls on a surface when some object comes between it and the source of light; (2) shade occurs on a surface when because of its relation to the direction of the rays of light it receives diminished light or no light at all. A typical shadow is illustrated by Fig. 294 and a typical instance of shade by Fig. 303.

Both shades and shadows are used in drawings and they can be obtained from orthographic projections by geometrical means employing what is known as the architectural convention. This convention is an assumption that the rays of light from the sun (taken as parallel rays) come downwards from the left-hand side at an angle of 45 degrees to the horizontal in elevation, and across from the left-hand side at an angle of 45 degrees to the vertical plane in plan—see Fig. 292. The resulting angle of light with the ground (horizontal plane) is therefore 35 degrees 16 minutes as illustrated by Fig. 292A.

The convention is a reasonable one as it corresponds to average natural conditions, and has the advantage of (1), giving shadows the width and height of which are in most cases the same as the projection or recess which causes them, and (2) making the plotting easy as it can be done entirely with tee-square and 45-degree set-square.

Usually, shades and shadows can be found from a combined consideration of elevation and plan, although in some cases they can be found from elevation and section. The following examples illustrate the application of the method:

Fig. 293 shows a vertical plane in plan and elevation with a point, P and P^1, at some distance in front of it. The position of the "shadow" of the point on the plane is found by drawing from P across at an angle of 45 degrees to the plane, projecting vertically to the elevation to cut a line drawn downwards at 45 degrees from P^1. The intersection, P^2, is the "shadow" point of the plane. It will be seen from the diagram how the position can also be found by a projection from the section.

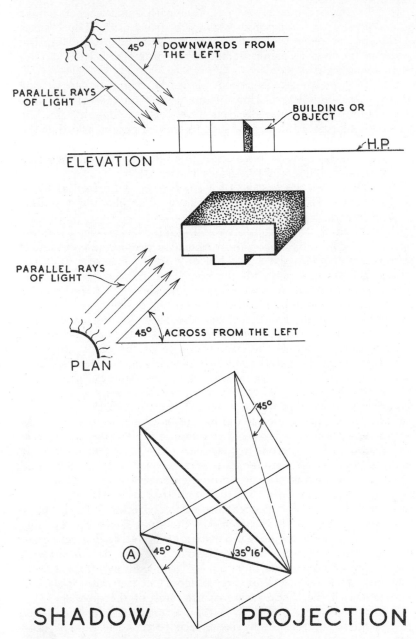

45° DOWNWARDS FROM THE LEFT

PARALLEL RAYS OF LIGHT

BUILDING OR OBJECT

H.P.

ELEVATION

PARALLEL RAYS OF LIGHT

45° ACROSS FROM THE LEFT

PLAN

45°

Ⓐ 45°

35°16'

SHADOW PROJECTION

Fig. 292

Fig. 294 shows a similar vertical plane with a smaller rectangular plane parallel to it and some distance in front of it. The shadow of the smaller plane on the larger plane is found by plotting the shadow positions of points at the four corners and then joining them by straight lines.

Fig. 295 shows two vertical planes at right-angles to one another, and how the shadow of one is cast on the other. Note that the outline of a shadow cast by a vertical edge or "line" is also vertical over a flat surface seen in true elevation, and that the outline of a shadow cast by a horizontal edge at right-angles to the true vertical plane is at an angle of 45 degrees (in the direction of the rays of light) on any surface in elevation.

Fig. 296 shows the casting of a shadow by a horizontal plane projecting forward from a vertical plane. The plotting is similar to that in Fig. 294.

Fig. 297 shows the shadow in a rectangular recess, e.g. a window opening and Fig. 298, the shadow cast by a projecting rectangular solid on a vertical plane, e.g. a balcony on the face of a building.

Fig. 299 shows a circular vertical plane parallel to and some distance in front of another plane. The shadow of the circular plane could be found by plotting the shadow positions of a number of points about its circumference and then joining them by a freehand curve. As will be seen, however, the outline of the shadow is the same as the circumference of the plane, and it is therefore easier to plot the shadow position of the centre of the plane and to describe a circle from it of the same radius.

Fig. 300 shows the shadow cast in a circular recess, e.g. bull's-eye window opening. Again, the centre of the front of the opening is plotted on or in the same plane as the back of the recess and an arc of radius equal to that of the opening is described as shown. The shadow of the reveal in plan can only be found accurately to a large scale. A number of points below the lower left-hand 45-degree tangent to the circumference in elevation are marked, and lines from them are drawn downwards at 45 degrees to cut the circumference, and vertical projections are made to the plan. The same points are also projected to the outer face of the opening in plan and from them lines are drawn across at 45 degrees to cut the corresponding lines already drawn. A line drawn through these intersections gives the outline of the shadow on the reveal. The line starts at the 45-degree tangent on the outer face and connects with the shadow line on the back of the recess.

Fig. 301 shows the shadow cast by a horizontal circular plane on a vertical surface. The procedure is to plot the shadow positions of a number of points on the circumference and then to join them by a curved line. It will be seen that the outline of the shadow is an ellipse.

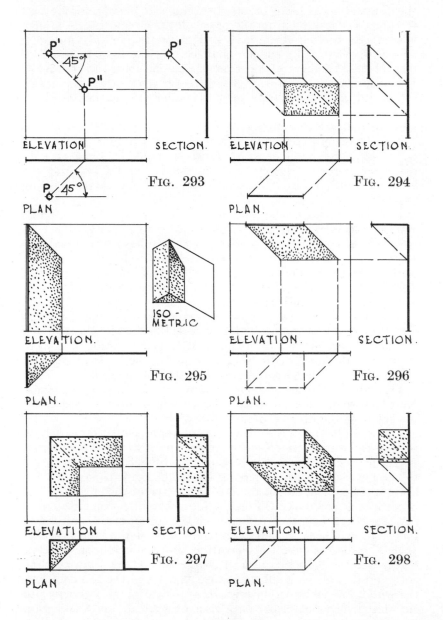

ELEVATION   SECTION.   FIG. 293

P'   45°   P'

P"

P   45°

PLAN

ELEVATION.   SECTION.   FIG. 294

PLAN.

ELEVATION.   ISO-METRIC   FIG. 295

PLAN.

ELEVATION.   SECTION.   FIG. 296

PLAN.

ELEVATION   SECTION.   FIG. 297

PLAN

ELEVATION.   SECTION.   FIG. 298

PLAN.

Fig. 302 shows the shadow cast in a recess with segmental head.

Fig. 303 shows the shade on a vertical cylinder according to the convention as used for the foregoing. It is obtained by projecting a vertical line from the point on the circumference in plan where the direction of the rays of light are tangential. Actually, of course, there is no sudden change from the light to the dark part of the cylinder and consequently no hard edge to the shade. It is convenient, however, in most cases to give a definite outline.

The outline of the shadow of the cylinder cast on the horizontal plane is shown superimposed on the diagram with construction lines to indicate the plotting.

Fig. 304 shows the shade on a horizontal cylinder. It is given by a 45-degree tangent in the direction of the light rays to the circumference in section. The outline of the plan of the cylinder on the horizontal plane is also shown with the plotting indicated.

Fig. 305 illustrates the casting of a shadow by a post which is standing some distance in front of a wall with a plinth. The construction lines show the plotting, which follows the procedure already described. Note that on plan the shadow of the post continues without break along the ground and the top surface of the plinth, but in elevation the projection of the plinth causes a break in the vertical lines of the shadow.

Fig. 306 illustrates a shadow cast on an inclined plane, e.g. the shadow cast by a chimney stack on a pitched roof. The plotting is made by projections from the elevation and section as shown. Note that the lines of the shadow cast by the vertical edges of the stack are inclined parallel to the pitch of the roof.

Fig. 307 illustrates various shadows on a three-arch loggia. Note that to find the outline of the arches in shadow it is necessary to plot both the inner and outer faces.

Fig. 308 illustrates the shadow in plan and elevation cast by a wall at right-angle to a flight of steps, and also the shadows cast by return steps. The latter presents no difficulties. With regard to the former, however, reference should be made to the pictorial sketch to help the visualisation of the shape of the shadow. The procedure is as follows: On plan a line in the direction of the light rays, i.e. at 45 degrees, is drawn from the corner of the wall across the steps. Where the line cuts the risers of the steps vertical projections are made to the elevation, and the line of the shadow of the vertical edge of the wall is represented by a zig-zag line going up the risers and along the treads. From the top corner of the wall a line is drawn downwards on elevation at 45 degrees to cut the zig-zag line either on a riser or a tread. In the diagram the intersection occurs on a riser. The intersection is the shadow point of the corner of the wall, and the outline of the shadow in

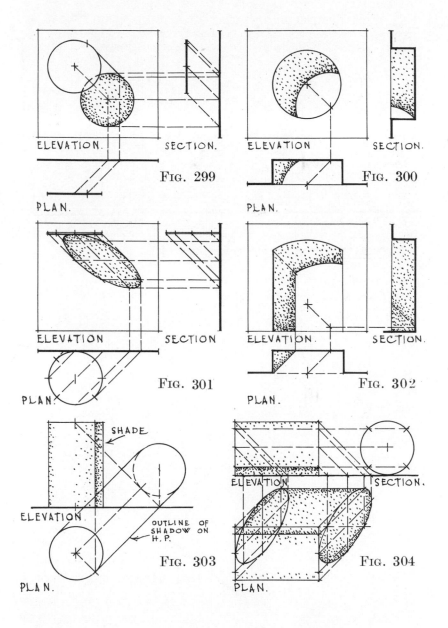

ELEVATION.   SECTION.

FIG. 299

PLAN.

ELEVATION   SECTION.

FIG. 300

PLAN.

ELEVATION   SECTION

FIG. 301

PLAN.

ELEVATION.   SECTION.

FIG. 302

PLAN.

SHADE

ELEVATION.

OUTLINE OF
SHADOW ON
H. P.

FIG. 303

PLAN.

ELEVATION   SECTION.

FIG. 304

PLAN.

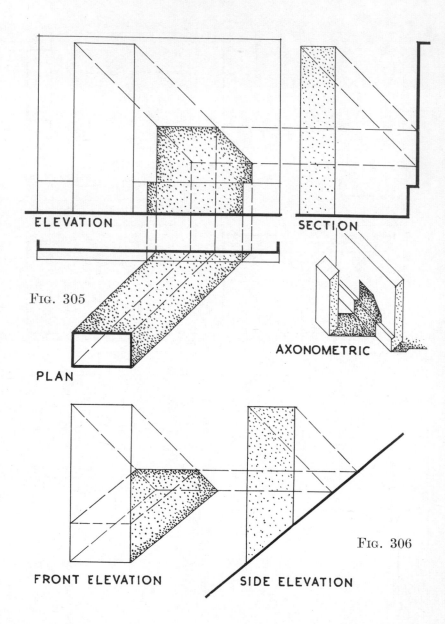

ELEVATION

SECTION

Fig. 305

PLAN

AXONOMETRIC

FRONT ELEVATION

SIDE ELEVATION

Fig. 306

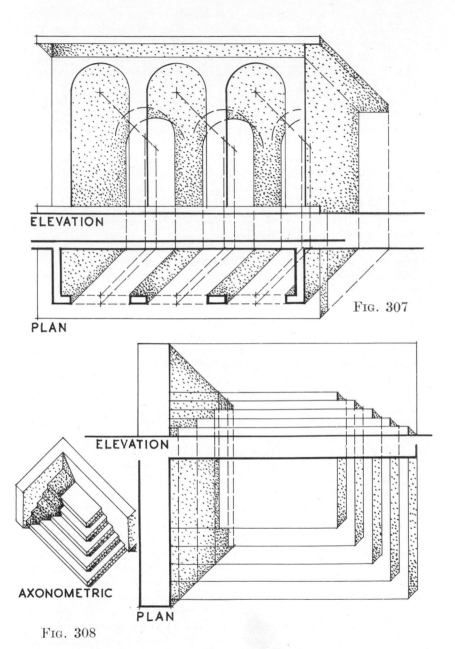

ELEVATION

PLAN

FIG. 307

ELEVATION

AXONOMETRIC

PLAN

FIG. 308

elevation is then complete. To complete the outline on plan vertical projections are made from the elevation where the 45-degree line cuts the lines of the treads.

Fig. 309 illustrate the shadows on a recessed door with a square canopy over. The construction lines and the pictorial sketch explain the plottings.

Fig. 310 illustrates the shadow cast by a square block resting on a cylinder, e.g. an abacus on a column. The shadow is found by taking a number of points along the lower front edge of the block and plotting their shadow positions in elevation, and then joining them by a curved line. Note that the part of the shadow line cast by the return edge of the block must appear as a straight line at 45 degrees on the elevation. ˙ The shadow merges into the shade which occurs on the cylinder as previously described. The outline of the shadow of the figure on the horizontal plane is superimposed on the diagram.

Fig. 311 shows the method of finding the shade on a sphere. The plan and elevation are drawn and a number of zones are determined—the zones of the lower half of the sphere in elevation corresponding to those of the lower half. A series of 45-degree lines in the direction of the light rays are drawn across the plan —it is most convenient to draw them tangential to the lines of the zones. Where these 45-degree lines intersect the zone lines projections are made to the elevation so that a series of curves can be plotted representing parallel cuts of the sphere. Lines at 45 degrees in the direction of the light rays in elevation are drawn tangential to the curves, and by drawing through the tangent points the line of the shade is traced. Projection can be made from the elevation to the plan to plot the line of shade in plan.

Fig. 312 illustrates the shadow of a semi-circular niche. It will be realised that the shadow is cast by the left-hand edge and the top edge of the front face as far as the 45-degree tangent on the right-hand side. The head of the niche in elevation is divided into a number of zones which are projected to the plan. A number of lines at 45 degrees in the direction of the light rays are then taken across the plan and, with the help of the zone lines, are plotted on the elevation. The intersections of these 45-degree lines with the front face on plan are projected up to the elevation from whence lines at 45 degrees in the direction of the light rays are drawn downwards to intersect the corresponding lines already plotted. By drawing through the intersection with a curved line the outline of the shadow can be completed as shown.

The above examples, although confined to elementary exercises, illustrate the bases of all shade and shadow projections, and meet all usual requirements.

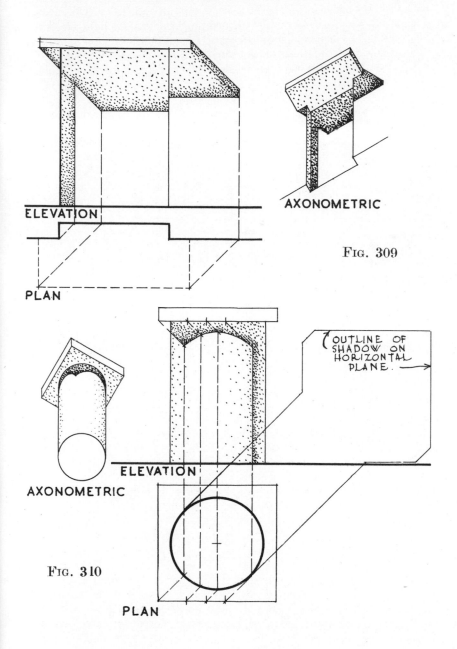

ELEVATION

AXONOMETRIC

PLAN

FIG. 309

AXONOMETRIC

ELEVATION

OUTLINE OF SHADOW ON HORIZONTAL PLANE.

FIG. 310

PLAN

Fig. 313 is a reproduction of an actual example sheet prepared by a student. The subject of the rendering of shades and shadows cannot be dealt with here, but for ordinary purposes a light neutral colour wash or careful pencil shading is sufficient.

In Fig. 172 the shadows shown in the perspective were first worked out on elevation and then set up in perspective along with the drawing.

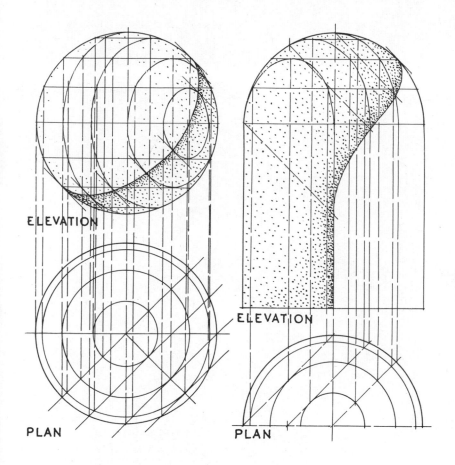

ELEVATION

PLAN

ELEVATION

PLAN

FIG. 311   FIG. 312

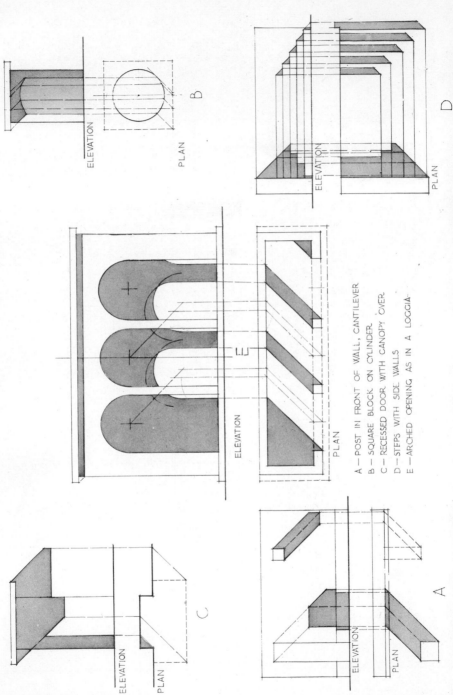

ELEVATION

PLAN

B

ELEVATION

PLAN

D

ELEVATION

E

PLAN

A — POST IN FRONT OF WALL, CANTILEVER.
B — SQUARE BLOCK ON CYLINDER.
C — RECESSED DOOR WITH CANOPY OVER.
D — STEPS WITH SIDE WALLS.
E — ARCHED OPENING AS IN A LOGGIA.

ELEVATION

PLAN

C

ELEVATION

PLAN

A

Fig. 313. STUDENT'S DRAWING SHOWING VARIOUS EXERCISES IN SHADOW PROJECTION, THE SHADES AND SHADOWS BEING INDICATED BY MEANS OF A WATER COLOUR WASH

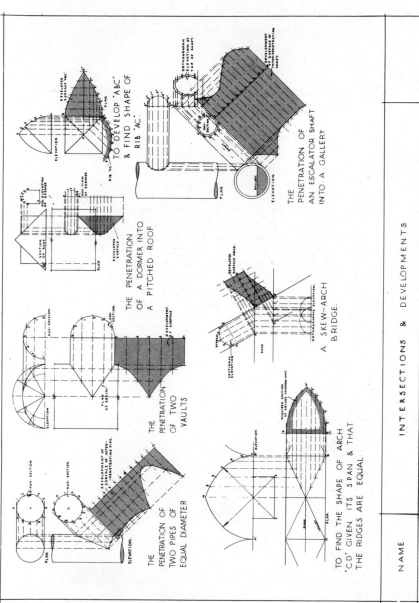

TO DEVELOP 'ABC'
& FIND SHAPE OF
RIB 'AC'

THE PENETRATION OF
AN ESCALATOR SHAFT
INTO A GALLERY

THE PENETRATION
OF A DORMER INTO
A PITCHED ROOF

A SKEW-ARCH
BRIDGE.

THE PENETRATION
OF TWO
VAULTS

THE PENETRATION OF
TWO PIPES OF
EQUAL DIAMETER

TO FIND THE SHAPE OF ARCH
'CD' GIVEN ITS SPAN & THAT
THE RIDGES ARE EQUAL.

INTERSECTIONS & DEVELOPMENTS

NAME

FIG. 314. STUDENT'S DRAWING OF EXERCISES DEALING WITH INTERSECTIONS
AND DEVELOPMENTS OF SURFACES

Union of Lancashire and Cheshire Institutes

SENIOR BUILDING COURSE (FIRST YEAR)
AND
COURSE FOR BRICKLAYERS AND MASONS (THIRD YEAR)

BUILDING GEOMETRY

1. The elevation of the keystone of a semi-elliptical arch is shown
in Fig. 1. The joint lines CD and EF are normals to the curve and
each is 1 ft. long. Construct the figure geometrically, to a scale of 1 in.
to 1 ft., and indicate on your drawing the length L in feet and inches.

2. The soffit line, ABC, of a segmental arch is shown in Fig. 2.
Construct the curve geometrically to the sizes shown. Given that the
span AC represents a distance of 3 ft., (a) construct an open divided
scale to measure feet and inches, and (b) figure on your drawing the
radius, in feet and inches, of the arc ABC.

3. A square plot of land is divided into two portions, P and Q, by
a fence $ABCD$, as shown in Fig. 3. It is desired to replace this fence
by a straight one, commencing at the corner D, which is to leave
unaltered the areas of P and Q respectively. Draw the figure. Determine by a geometrical method the position of the new fence, and figure
its length on your drawing. Scale: 1 in. to 100 ft.

4. The plan and elevation of a building stone are given in Fig. 4.
Draw these views, and add an elevation when viewed in the direction
of the arrow. Scale: $1\frac{1}{2}$ in. to 1 ft.

5. Draw an isometric view of the building stone shown in Fig. 4.
Scale: $1\frac{1}{2}$ in. to 1 ft.

6. Two elevations of a roof are given in Fig. 5. Draw these views,
from them project a plan, and develop the surface marked P. Scale:
$\frac{1}{4}$ in. to 1 ft.

7. The plan and a normal cross-section of a roof are shown in Fig. 6.
Draw these views, and add an elevation of the roof when viewed at
right angles to the end EF. Scale: $\frac{1}{8}$ in. to 1 ft.

8. The curved roof of a dormer intersects a plane pitched roof as
shown in Fig. 7. Draw the given views, to a scale of $\frac{1}{2}$ in. to 1 ft., and
develop the cylindrical surface marked S up to its edge of intersection
with the plane roof surface.

9. A small roof is in the form of a pyramid 4 ft. high, its base being
a regular octagon, measuring 8 ft. between each pair of parallel sides.
Draw its plan and elevation, develop one of its triangular surfaces,
and mark on your drawing the exact length of one of the hip rafters.
Scale: $\frac{3}{8}$ in. to 1 ft.

10. A building, rectangular in plan, is 20 ft. long, and 10 ft. wide.
It is covered by a hipped roof and all four surfaces are inclined at
45 deg. to the H.P. Draw its plan and end elevation, determine the true
length of a common rafter, and a hip rafter. Scale: 1 in. to 5 ft.

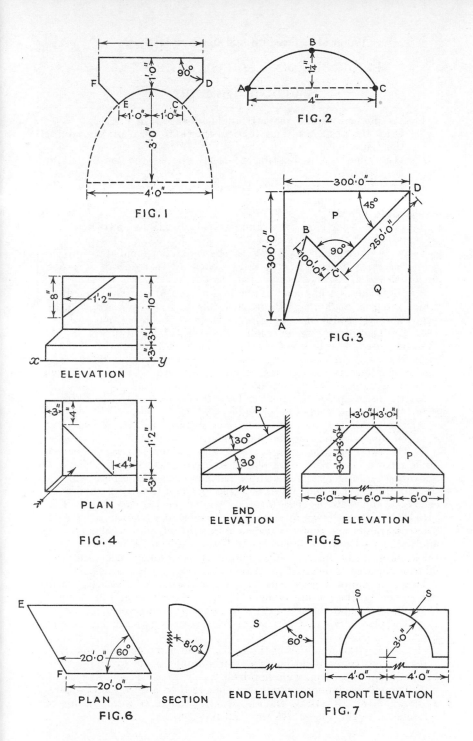

FIG. 1

FIG. 2

FIG. 3

ELEVATION

PLAN

FIG. 4

END
ELEVATION

ELEVATION

FIG. 5

PLAN

SECTION

FIG. 6

END ELEVATION

FRONT ELEVATION

FIG. 7

SENIOR BUILDING COURSE (THIRD YEAR)

BUILDING GEOMETRY

1. Two projections of a plane triangle are shown in Fig. 1.
(a) Draw the horizontal and vertical traces of the plane containing the figure.
(b) Determine the inclination of the plane of the figure to the horizontal plane.
(c) Find the true shape of the triangle.

2. An 18 in. deep parabolic arch springs from two stone abutments, as shown in Fig. 2.

Set out the inside curve as a true parabola, with the joints at A and B truly normal to the curve.

Draw the outer curve *parallel* to the inner one, and draw in the joints of three arch stones at crown each 12 in. wide at intrados, including the key-stone. Scale: $\frac{1}{4}$ in. to 1 ft.

3. Fig. 3 shows a moulded plinth and a vertical marginal moulding which intersect at 90 deg. Reproduce this diagram, full size, and, by projection, determine the elevation of the line of intersection at I.

4. The plan of an existing roof, marked E, is shown in Fig. 4. At N a new shed is to be erected, 15 ft. wide with a lean-to roof of the same rise as E and coinciding in the level at eaves and ridge. The new roof intersects the existing one in a valley at VY. If the pitch of the existing roof is 30 deg., find:
(a) the pitch of the new roof and the true length of the valley,
(b) the dihedral angle for the valley VY,
(c) the bevels for the foot of the jack rafters—as at JR—so as to fit upon the existing roof boarding.

5. The two diagrams (a) and (b) in Fig. 5 show two cases where a circle (shown dotted) is to be placed so as to pass through a point P and to touch tangentially the three parts of circles forming a window design. By construction, determine the centre of the required circle in each case, and draw the circle accurately in position. Scale: $\frac{3}{4}$ in. to 1 ft.

6. The plans of two intersecting corridors are shown in Fig. 6. These corridors are roofed with barrel vaults of semicircular section and springing from the same level. If the vaulting is uniformly 1 ft. thick, project the lines of intersection of the two exterior and two interior surfaces of *one* roof junction only. Scale: $\frac{3}{4}$ in. to 1 ft.

7. Fig. 7 shows a cast iron base for a stanchion. Set this up in perspective on the picture plane PP, the spectator being 8 ft. distant from the plane and the eye-level 5 ft. above ground-level.

8. The plan of the foot of a geometrical stair is given in Fig. 8, and need not be re-drawn.
(a) Develop the step lines of the wall and outer strings for a 6-in. rise.
(b) Set out the main outline of a scroll suitable for the given position, as a terminal to a $3\frac{1}{2}$-in. wide handrail.

9. Three 6-in. diameter pipes are connected to a 9-in. metal sphere as shown in Fig. 9. Draw the elevation of the three intersections of the pipes with the sphere. Scale: half full-size.

10. A stone doorway 4 ft. wide is formed in a wall 18 in. thick and curved in a plan to a radius of 8 ft. The *elevation* of the head of the opening is semi-circular and the jambs are parallel. If the stone arch is formed of seven units, set out the arch completely and obtain the bed and face moulds of *one* of the voussoirs adjoining the key-stone.

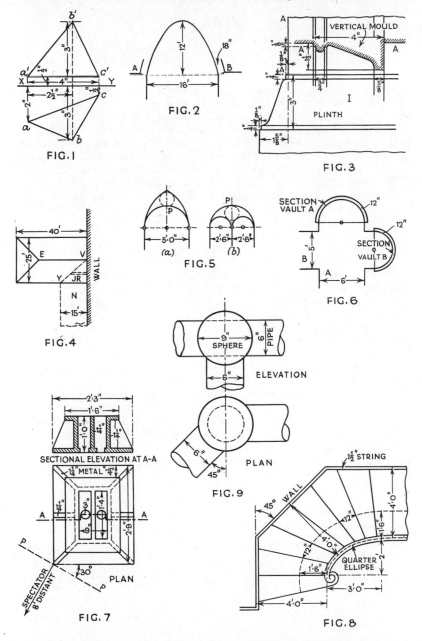

FIG.1

FIG.2

FIG.3

FIG.4

FIG.5

FIG.6

FIG.7

FIG.8

FIG.9

Union of Lancashire and Cheshire Institutes

ADVANCED BUILDING COURSE

GEOMETRY

1. Fig. 1 shows two projections of a plane triangle.
 (a) Determine the horizontal and vertical traces of the plane containing the triangle.
 (b) Find the inclination of the surface of the triangle to (i) the horizontal, and (ii) the vertical plane.
 (c) Find the true angle between the edges AB and AC.

2. Fig. 2 gives the plan of the centre line CL óf a handrail wreath at an acute-angled turn in a stair. The slopes of the tangents are also given. Assume a handrail 3 in. wide and $2\frac{1}{2}$ in. thick, and
 (a) develop the face mould for the wreath, allowing 4 in. shanks;
 (b) determine the twist bevels for the ends of the wreath;
 (c) find the minimum thickness of material to produce a fully squared wreath.
 Scale: quarter full-size.

3. The elevation of the hood of a niche is a semi-ellipse of 4 ft. span and 1 ft. 8 in. rise. The plan of the niche is a semi-circle. Set out the hood, to a scale of 1 in. to 1 ft., and indicate a suitable geometrical form of construction for the use of stone. Obtain the face and bed moulds for any one of the voussoirs.

4. Fig. 3 shows the plan of a curved wall which is part of a hollow cylinder. The wall is pierced by a bull's-eye window which is circular in elevation at the sight edge, marked AB, and the jambs are splayed at the springing of the upper arch, the complete surface of the reveal being cuneoidal. Draw plan and elevation of the upper half of the window, showing the stone voussoirs. Develop the face and bed moulds for one stone. Scale: 1 in. to 1 ft.

5. Fig. 4 shows the plan of an elevated road, formed over irregular ground by tipping. The road is 40 ft. above the horizontal datum line at A and rises uniformly to a height of 60 ft. above datum at B. Draw a plan of the road, showing the slopes and formation of the tipped material if the sides of the embankment rise 1 ft. 6 in. vertical in 1 ft. horizontal. Use a horizontal scale of $\frac{1}{4}$ in. to 10 *yards* and a vertical scale of $\frac{1}{4}$ in. to 10 *feet*.

6. Fig. 5 shows the plan and elevation of an entrance lobby opening on to a small hall. Draw a perspective view on a plane parallel to the wall AB and 2 ft. in front of it. The position of the spectator is shown at V and the height of the point of vision is 5 ft. Scale for plans: $\frac{1}{2}$ in. to 1 ft.

214

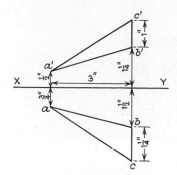

FIG. 1

X — a' — 3" — b' — c' ... labels: c', b', a', ½", ¾", 3", 1½", 1¼", 1", a, b, c, 1¼", Y

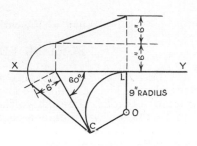

X — 60° — 6" — 6" — 6" — L — 9" RADIUS — C — O — Y

FIG. 2

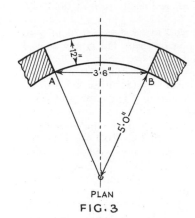

12" — A — 3'6" — B — 5'0" — PLAN

FIG. 3

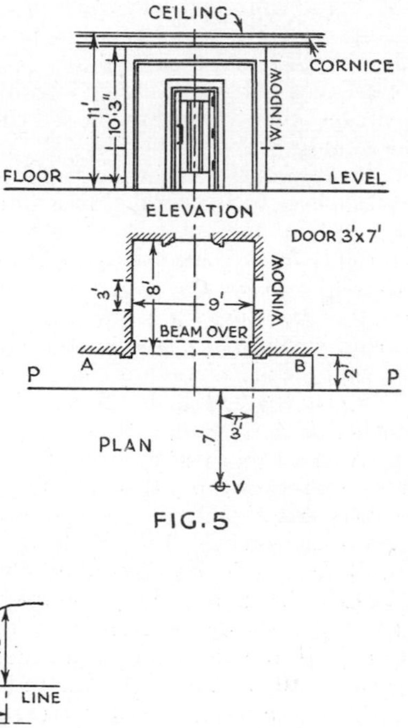

CEILING
CORNICE
WINDOW
11" 10'3"
FLOOR — LEVEL
ELEVATION

DOOR 3'x7'
3' 8' 9' WINDOW
BEAM OVER
P — A — B — P
2'
7' 3'
PLAN
V

FIG. 5

SECTION
10' 20' 20' 25' 40'
DATUM — 100 YDS. — 60 YDS. — 90 YDS. — B — LINE
PLAN
100 YDS.
10 YDS.
A

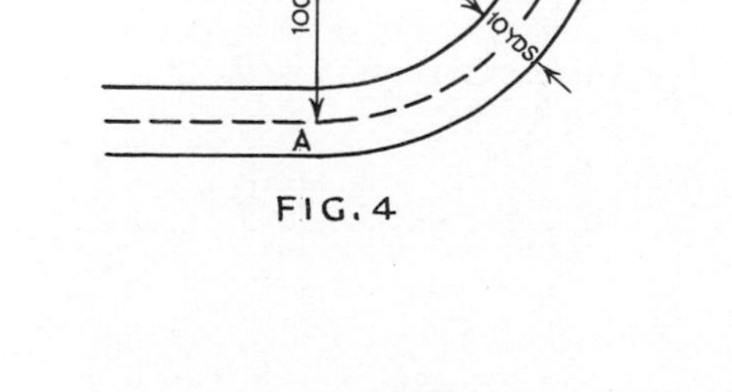

FIG. 4

Union of Educational Institutions

BUILDING GEOMETRY: S1

1. Fig. 1 represents the plan of a piece of building land *A B C D E*. Draw the figure to a scale of 1 in. to 10 ft., and construct a triangle equal in area to it. Write down the area of the triangle in sq. ft.

2. To full size scale draw a regular five-sided figure *A B C D E* of 2 in. side. Measure and write down the number of degrees in the angle *A B C*.
Draw the inscribed circle of the figure and measure the radius.
Show clearly all points of contact.

3. Fig. 2 shows the elevation of a mantelpiece. Draw this to a scale of 1 in. to 1 ft., and by radial projection, reduce it proportionately, making *A B* equal to 2 ft. 6 in.

4. A piece of moulding cut against a wall at *A B* is shown in plan elevation and section Fig. 3. To full size scale draw the true shape of the moulding at *A B*.

5. A stone arch 12 in. on the face is 4 ft. span and 1 ft. 6 in. rise. The inner curve is a semi-ellipse and the arch is made up of five stones. To a scale of 1 in. to 1 ft. draw the inner curve of the arch and show two joints of the arch normal to the curve.

6. Fig. 4 shows the plan and unfinished elevation of a piece of stone coping at the angle of a building. To a scale of 1 in. to 1 ft. draw the plan and complete the elevation. Now draw a new elevation when looking in the direction of the arrow *E*.

7. Referring to Fig. 4. To a scale of $1\frac{1}{2}$ in. to 1 ft. make an isometric drawing of the coping. All construction lines must be left visible.

8. A small roof in the form of a square based pyramid is cut by the plane surface of a roof as shown in plan and elevation Fig. 5. Complete the plan and find the true shape of the section at *A C*. Draw the true shape of the surface *A B*. Scale: $\frac{1}{2}$ in. to 1 ft.

9. Referring to Fig. 5, obtain the true shape of the surfaces at *M* and along *B C* above the plane roof surface. Scale: $\frac{1}{2}$ in. to 1 ft.

10. Fig. 6 shows the plan of a hipped roof cut against a wall at *A B*. Surfaces *M* and *N* are at 45 deg. and *P* is at 60 deg. pitch. To a scale of $\frac{1}{4}$ in. to 10 ft. draw the plan and develop the surfaces *N* and *P*.

11. The elevation vertical cross section and incomplete plan of a simple air-raid shelter are shown in Fig. 7. Complete the plan to a scale of $\frac{1}{2}$ in. to 1 ft. and show the true shape of the section made by the plane *M N* when looking in the direction of the arrow at *E*.

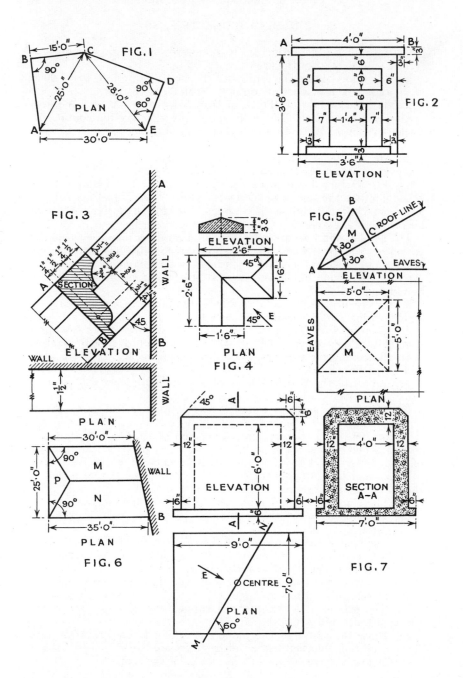

BUILDING GEOMETRY: S2

1. Fig. 1 shows the outline for a tracery window in an ogee arch.
   (a) Draw the line of the arch.
   (b) Using loci obtain the centres of the circles A and B, draw them and show all points of contact. Scale: 1 in. to 1 ft.

2. The plan is shown in Fig. 2 of two roof surfaces M and N intersecting in a hip. Face N is inclined at 30 deg. to the horizontal. To a scale of 1 in. to 10 ft. draw the plan and obtain:
   (a) The inclination of face M to the horizontal.
   (b) The true length of the hip A B.
   (c) The true angle between the faces M and N.

3. A B C D Fig. 3 represents the plan of a plot of building land. P is a point on the side A D. Draw the plan to a scale of 1 in. to 10 ft. and from P draw two lines, PS and PT, which shall divide the plot into three equal areas.

4. The plan and incomplete elevation of a raking mould returned at A and cut against a wall at B are shown in Fig. 4. The true section of the mould is shown at C D. To full size scale complete the elevation showing the raking mould returned at A and the intersection of the mould and wall at B.

5. Make a neat isometric drawing of the stone cap shown in plan and elevation Fig. 5. Scale: 1 in. to 1 ft.

6. An area A B C D Fig. 6 is to be covered with a roof having a small flat. Faces M, N and T are 45 deg. pitch, and P is 60 deg. pitch. A small opening for a chimney-stack is shown in face T. To a scale of 1 in. to 10 ft.:
   (a) Complete the plan of the roof, clearly indicating the position of the flat.
   (b) Develop the surfaces P and T and obtain the true shape of the chimney-stack opening.

7. An architrave is cut against a splayed plinth block as shown in front and end elevation Fig. 7. To full size scale complete the elevation of the intersection of the architrave with the splayed face of the plinth.

8. A small square based turret is cut by the plane face of a roof as shown in Fig. 8. To a scale of ½ in. to 1 ft. draw:
   (a) The plan of the portion of the turret above the roof surface.
   (b) The true shape of the section of the turret made by the roof surface.
   (c) The true shape of the face of the turret marked P.

9. Two equilateral vaults intersect as shown in elevation and incomplete plan Fig. 9. To a scale of ½ in. to 1 ft.:
   (a) Complete the plan showing clearly the lines of intersection.
   (b) Develop the surface marked P.

10. The plan and elevation of the hipped end of a roof are shown in Fig. 10. To full size scale:
    (a) Draw the traces of the plane containing the roof surface, and find its inclination to the horizontal plane.
    (b) Obtain the true shape of the surface of the roof.

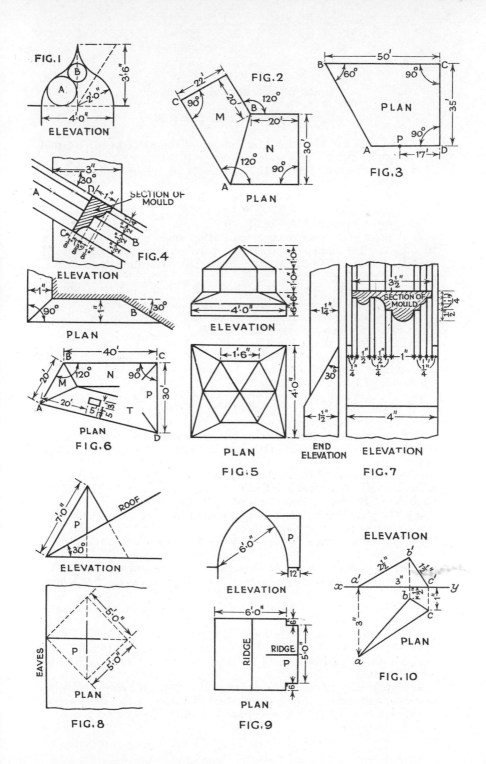

FIG.1
ELEVATION
3'-6"
4'-0"
A
B
2'-0"

FIG.2
PLAN
C 90° 22'
120°
M 20
B 20'
120° N 30'
90°
A

FIG.3
PLAN
50'
B 60° 90° C
35'
P 90°
A 17' D

FIG.4
SECTION OF MOULD
3"
30°
D 1"
A
C
B
6"×1¼"
6"×3½"
6"×½"
1¼"
2¼"
2¼"
1½"
ELEVATION
1"
90°
½"
B 30°
PLAN

FIG.5
ELEVATION
4'-0"
6"·6"·1'-0"·1'-0"
PLAN
1'·6"
4'-0"
FIG.5

END ELEVATION
1¼"
30°
1½"

FIG.7
SECTION OF MOULD
3½"
1½"·1½"·¼"
½"·¼" 2¼"·2½" 1" 1¼"·¼"
30°
1½"
4"
ELEVATION

FIG.6
PLAN
40'
B C
120° N 90°
20' M
A 20' 5"·5/3"
T P 30'
D
FIG.6

FIG.8
ELEVATION
7'-0" P ROOF
30°
PLAN
EAVES
5'·0" 5'·0"
P

FIG.9
ELEVATION
6'·0" P
12"
PLAN
6'·0"
RIDGE
RIDGE P
5'·0"
6"
6"

FIG.10
ELEVATION
x a' 2½" 3" b' 1½" c' y
3"
a
b
c
PLAN
FIG.10

BUILDING GEOMETRY: S3

1. The plan and elevation of a portion of the hipped end of a roof are shown in Fig. 1. To a scale of 1 in. to 10 ft. draw:
   (a) The horizontal and vertical traces of the plane containing the figure.
   (b) The inclination of this plane to the horizontal and vertical planes of projection.
   (c) The true shape of the figure.

2. A path 10 ft. wide meets a road at an angle of 60 deg. as shown in Fig. 2. The rounded corners are parabolic arcs tangential at A and B, C and D. To a scale of ¼ in. to 1 ft. construct these curves, and show clearly the method used.

3. The incomplete plan and elevation of part of a raking mould are shown in Fig. 3. An enlarged section of the mould at A B is shown also. To full size scale complete the elevation up to CD, and draw:
   (a) The true shape of the mould at CD.
   (b) The plan of the end of CD.

4. Fig. 4 shows the elevation and plan of a bay-window soffit. A section at A B is also shown. All horizontal sections are parallel. To a scale of 1 in. to 1 ft. draw:
   (a) The plan and project an elevation and obtain the correct position of the ribs.
   (b) The development of the face abcd.

5. Draw to a scale three-quarter full size a single line volute of three convolutions. The overall width is 8 in. and the diameter of the eye is 1 in.

6. A lean-to roof 7 ft. up the slope and 45 deg. pitch is intersected by a similar roof to form a valley 8 ft. long. The eaves in plan are at an angle of 120 deg. Draw to a scale ½ in. to 1 ft.:
   (a) The plan of the roof surfaces showing the valley and obtain the pitch of the other roof.
   (b) Obtain the angle between the roof surfaces, i.e., the dihedral angle.

7. Fig. 5 shows the plan of a staircase with a semi-circular well. The fliers have 11 in. tread and 6 in. rise. To a scale of 1 in. to 1 ft. draw:
   (a) The development of the well string.
   (b) Show clearly the springing lines SS and the joints between the main and well strings.

8. A conical turret is intersected by the corner of a hipped roof, as shown in plan and elevation Fig. 6. To a scale of ½ in. to 1 ft. draw the plan and elevation of the intersection of the roof surfaces and the conical turret.

9. Two stone pillars and a portion of a wall are shown in plan elevation and section Fig. 7. To a scale of ½ in. to 1 ft. set up a perspective drawing of them in accordance with the particulars given.

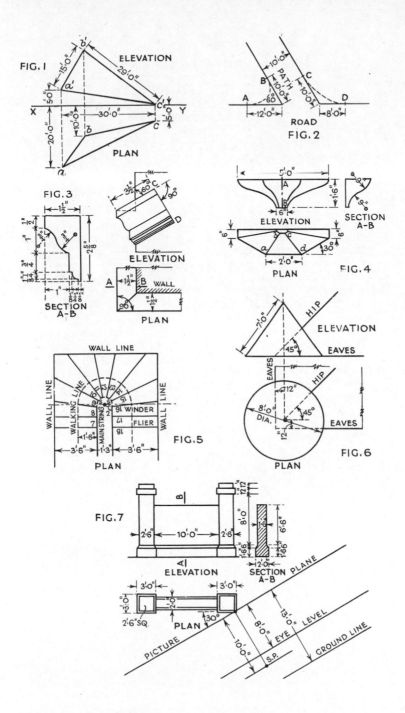

FIG. 1

ELEVATION

PLAN

FIG. 2

PATH

ROAD

FIG. 3

ELEVATION

SECTION A-B

WALL

PLAN

FIG. 4

ELEVATION

SECTION A-B

PLAN

FIG. 5

WALL LINE

WALKING LINE

MAIN STRING

WINDER

FLIER

PLAN

FIG. 6

ELEVATION

HIP

EAVES

EAVES

HIP

EAVES

PLAN

FIG. 7

ELEVATION

SECTION PLANE A-B

PLAN

PICTURE PLANE

EYE LEVEL

GROUND LINE

S.P.

City and Guilds of London Institute

CARPENTRY AND JOINERY

Intermediate Examination

1. The plan and side elevation are given of a roof in Fig. 1. Calculate the net area of the roof surface.

2. Design an architrave moulding $1\frac{1}{2}$ in. by 3 in. wide, embodying the following mouldings: ogee, ovolo, and cavetto, with the necessary fillets.

Also obtain the section of a moulding $2\frac{1}{4}$ in. wide which will intersect with the former moulding at right angles.

3. Obtain the net area of the surface of the roof, shown in plan, in Fig. 2. One end of the plan is formed by three sides of a regular octagon. The pitch of the roof is 45 deg.

4. The plan and elevation of a roof are shown in Fig. 3. The centres of the upper curves are in the line XX.

Obtain the outline of a corner rib and the development of one of the surfaces. Scale: $\frac{1}{2}$ in. to 1 ft.

5. A vertical architrave 3 in. wide by $1\frac{1}{2}$ in. thick has to mitre with a horizontal architrave $2\frac{1}{4}$ in. wide. Draw, full size, a suitable ogee section for the larger moulding and determine the section of the smaller moulding so that the two mouldings may properly intersect.

6. Draw in isometric projection the tenons on the end of a 8 in. by $1\frac{1}{8}$ in. bottom rail of a skylight. Scale: half full size.

7. Fig. 4 shows the section of a crown moulding. From the dimensions given draw:

    (a) a copy of the mould, full size;

    (b) an outline of a mould similar in all respects but with side A B 4 in. long.

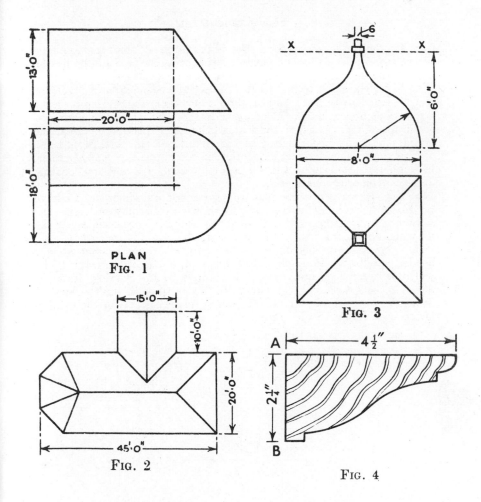

PLAN
Fig. 1

Fig. 3

Fig. 2

Fig. 4

City and Guilds of London Institute

CARPENTRY AND JOINERY

Final Examination

1. Obtain the following for a roof of ⅓rd pitch: (i) the backing of the hip rafter, (ii) bevels for the purlin to fit against the side and under the edge of the hip rafter, (iii) the top bevel of a jack rafter.

2. Using a scale of 1½ in. to 1 ft. obtain the face mould and bevels for the wreathed portion of a hand-rail for a quarter space landing connecting two flights of stairs. The centre line of the wreath in plan is a quadrant of a circle of 5 in. radius, and the faces of the risers are at the springing. Going of step 9 in., rise 7 in., hand-rail 3 in. thick, 4 in. wide.

3. A dome, semi-circular in section and octagonal in plan, is 15 ft. in diameter. Determine the shape of an angle rib and its backing, and give constructional details.

4. Fig. 1 represents the plan of two corridors which are to have brick-vaulted ceilings intersecting as shown by the dotted lines. The soffit of the vaulting of the narrower corridor is semi-circular. Make drawings to illustrate the necessary centring. Scale: ½ in. to 1 ft.

5. A splayed panelled lining is to be fitted around a semi-circular headed window at an angle of 120 deg. to the face of the frame. The width between the grooves for the linings in the window frame is 3 ft. 6 in., and the distance between the face of the wall and the window frame is 14 in. Obtain the moulds and bevels necessary for the making of the head lining. Scale: 1½ in. to 1 ft

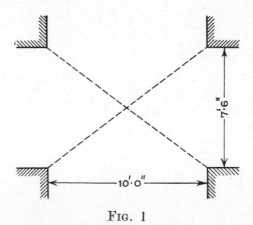

FIG. 1